*A
Harlequin
Romance*

Many of these titles are available at your local bookseller,
or through the Harlequin Reader Service.

For a free catalogue listing all available Harlequin Romances,
send your name and address to:

HARLEQUIN READER SERVICE,
M.P.O. Box 707, Niagara Falls, N.Y. 14302
Canadian address: Stratford, Ontario, Canada.

or use coupon at back of book.

SWEET SUNDOWN

by

MARGARET WAY

HARLEQUIN BOOKS   TORONTO
WINNIPEG

Original hard cover edition published in 1974
by Mills & Boon Limited.

© Margaret Way 1974

SBN 373-01880-0

Harlequin edition published May 1975

Printed in Canada

1880

CHAPTER ONE

EVER since she had been a little girl, her mother had promised her a trip to Sundown. 'You'll love it, my darling!' her mother would say, her beautiful eyes, dreamy, darkly enchanted, intent on other times, the chosen place. 'The house and the vineyards, the green hills and a cloudless sky. The settled peace! Why, it's the most wonderful place on earth, Gabby, my angel, you'll see! The vast spreads of lawn, like velvet, the poplars and the evergreens, our camellias, every variety you can think of—we had three gardeners when I was a child—and on the crest of the hill—Sundown. Sweet Sundown!' Drawing a deep breath, her voice tender, she had turned to her daughter, beauty and breeding legible in her face. 'After all, darling, it's your heritage too! Your great-grandfather built Sundown. Made a fortune from the vines!'

'Lost it too!' her father would say dryly, every time. Soft jibes for the most part, for love and indulgence shone out of his fine eyes. Just as it had been impossible for her mother to speak of her old family home dispassionately, it had been equally impossible for her cool, level-headed father to resist the sheer delight of provoking the beautiful Paula Lawrence that was. The brilliant butterfly who had passed up every splendid chance there was, in favour of the then struggling young architect, Drew Somerville. The marriage had shocked family and friend alike, seeming as it did to be a decided come-down. It was all very well to marry for love and he *was* terribly attractive, but what then?

Then, as to the end, the marriage had worked out, so that the countless pleasurable would-be excursions to Sundown had become a kind of game between her parents, maintained at that level, for their love was so real, so eloquent, it stood alone, with no need of support from the past. They lived for a future together with their adored only child. But from time to time, with the regularity of clockwork, her mother engrossed herself in some nebulous plans that would allow her daughter to see Sundown.

'When you're free of exams ... when Daddy isn't so madly involved with some V.I.P.'s house plans ... when I finish this wondrous painting of mine ... then we'll go. But it must be vintage time.' Gabriele turned her face sightlessly towards the dazzling, dipping wing of the Boeing. Her memory was flooded with all the old scenes. Scenes she imagined in her youthful tranquillity that would never come to an end. Her heart gave a little sickening lurch of pain. Her mother was still speaking with all the gay charm that was hers. 'I could never convey to you, darling, the excitement, the fascination of it all. Why, the whole estate comes to life. Swarms of itinerant workers moving along the laden vines. The exquisite bloom on the grapes. Ours was a quality vineyard, you know. As girls we knew the name, age and pedigree of all our vines. You *must* see the vintage in progress. The tastings, and out of the vigorous, bubbling vats ... a new wine. Wonderfully delicate. Robust. Who knows? It varies according to the amount of rain and sunshine. It's such a mystery, darling, and the outcome of a whole set of complicated procedures you must see for yourself. Wine, the joy of it! as my dear father used to say. Yes, I'm determined to show you now. We'll go!'

About this time in the conversation, her father would

6

rise to his lean six feet, caressing his wife's flawless cheek, his light, satirical tone rather devastating. 'Mightn't it be better, my own, if we waited for an invitation? Always supposing it comes. Gabby darling, how *old* are you now?' Then they would all laugh. Gabriele could still see the faint flush in her mother's cheeks, hear the soft, husky laugh. 'What? Wait for an invitation from my sister. My *own* sister!'

'Is she as pretty as you, Mamma?'

'Prettier. Why, darling, you can't imagine!'

Gabriele, the child, had looked to her father for confirmation, but the expression in his eyes had always puzzled her, a grim kind of amusement and something else. Somehow he must always have known. 'Your Aunt Camilla is a very beautiful woman, Gabby. A painted lady. But she can't hold a candle to your mother. In anything!'

'I can't think why you never took to Camilla,' her mother would answer, her face alight with wry humour. 'Everyone does. Trust you to be the exception!' But you could see how glad she was. 'Anyway, Camilla's way of life isn't ours!' ... *Thank God!* ... from her father. 'Why, she simply wouldn't have time to sit down and write, not with her mad round of engagements!'

Her father had continued to smile as if he had known. And he *must* have. The invitation had never come. Until now. Now when it scarcely mattered at all, she was going to Sundown, the lovely old Colonial mansion where her mother had been born. One of two sisters known to the society columns as the Beautiful Lawrence Girls—raven-haired, white-skinned, like two lovely magnolias. It was marvellous to have looks and style and what was even more important when one wished to create a legend or figure in the glossy magazines, a great deal of money. Even when the Lawrence fortunes were well on the wane, the house and the family name had enough of an aura to allow Camilla, the younger by three years, to land the biggest catch of the year—Paul Lynnton. Grandson of the industrial giant, Sir Joshua Lynnton. A merging of business interests, the ever-ready detractors, all wedding guests, had cynically said, for despite the bride's very real assets, it was public knowledge that Sir Joshua owned the company that had bought Old Man Lawrence out. The wine industry was expanding rapidly, a comparatively new field where Sir Joshua foresaw immense profits. Sundown, and the home vineyard, classified as 'first growth' went with the deal. A wedding present, allowing the bride to remain at her old family home, but a transfer of the deeds to Sir Joshua, an electrifying man (some said a monster) who had clawed his way up from errand boy at the age of twelve to one of the country's financial giants. A self-made, self-taught (he was hardest on those who had had a university education) multi-millionaire. Money made money, he had more than proved that, but fine, old houses like Sundown, with an aura of muted luxury and elegance, were not easy to come by.

Her grandfather must have thought so too, Gabriele thought quietly, for he had died a few months after leaving it. On her knees was an open copy of *Vogue* magazine, her eyes dropped to the glossy, full page photograph. Mrs. Paul Lynnton wears Givenchy. Well, no one could blame her for that. Givenchy would work wonders for any woman's confidence, and Aunt Camilla, quite obviously, would look well in a gunny sack. A petite brunette with a beautiful figure, she would be what ...? Thirty-eight. She looked nothing like it, but a flower child. Large dark eyes, spectacularly made up, very glamorous, very elegant, exquisitely sure of herself. *A painted lady?* She knew why her father said that. It was Mamma looking like Mamma had never done. The resemblance was striking. They must, in their girlhood, have been taken for twins. Her Aunt Camilla was very beautiful, sophistication and knowledge in those brilliant dark eyes, faintly tilted like the brows, but to Gabriele, she looked a little ... *over*-civilised? Artificial, perhaps, beside Mamma who had never pushed her beauty home but rather tended to understate it. 'But I've gone hopelessly primitive, darling!' she could hear her mother saying it, defending the washing and setting of her own lovely hair.

Long, heartbreaking months after her parents' tragic death in a road accident, she could still hear them talking to her, helping, guiding, lending consolation. The miracle was, she had not been with them on that day of fatal, beautiful placidity. It had been hot and dry, a summer dream. Her mother with her instant, gay way of making decisions had said: 'We're off!' which heralded a quick, sixty-minute trip to the tumbling surf of the Coast. Ten minutes before they left, a few of her friends had called in, precipitating a change of plans. She had gone with them—a monumental decision. It didn't bear thinking about. She couldn't, and for a long time wished herself into a long dark oblivion, day after day struggling bereft, with the pangs of bereavement; she kept herself moving, or immersed in her studies, in which, extraordinarily enough, she gained three distinctions, not realising that from both her parents she had inherited the precious legacy of a brave heart. The courageous spirit that rose, if shakily above adversity, aspects of her character had she known it, she would need at Sundown.

So engrossed was she in the full page coverage that

Gabriele missed the sudden appearance of the air hostess, and the slight, attractive drawl startled her.

'She's a real glamour girl, isn't she? And no chicken either! Which gives us all heart. Some of the other girls have travelled with her, but *I* never have, though she's in every magazine I seem to pick up. *Mrs. Paul Lynnton!*' There was envy and reverence in the husky drawl. 'Of course she's got tons of money! But tons! You'd need it to keep yourself looking like that. That dress must have cost the earth. Givenchy! It's like the breeze!'

'My aunt!' Gabriele found herself announcing into this recital. Involuntary, for all her instincts were for privacy.

'Your aunt?' The blue eyes opened wider and the soft, coral-tinted mouth fell open with shocked scepticism. 'Mrs. Paul Lynnton is *your* aunt?'

In happier days, Gabriele would most certainly have laughed, but then she only replied gravely. 'My mother's sister. My mother was, I think, far more beautiful, although superficially they're as alike as two pearls in a matched string.'

She *was* telling the truth! The air hostess looked again, harder this time, reappraising ... A tall girl, too slender, good legs, pale shining hair. Beautiful hair, if she was going to be fair, a silver-gilt stream, but she would have to do something about her whole style and her clothes, as pale and understated as she was. Gabriele was not a pretty girl by the air hostess's standards and tastes which were strictly in the modern idiom with the accent on lashings of what she called glamour. Like Mrs. Paul Lynnton, fabulous creature! It was a classic face looking back at her. Not *cold*, exactly, but very cool, rather withdrawn. No smiles and a thought too intelligent. The features were very finely modelled and really the eyes, grey like the rain, iridescent in their dark webbing of lashes, were exceptionally beautiful, but they had the disconcerting tendency to look through rather than at one. It very nearly irked her. She wouldn't easily attract the boys, the older girl thought complacently, secure in her own vivacious personality. But there she was wrong, missing as she did, the deep implication of just the simple past tense. *My mother was ...*

There was a dangerous fragility about Gabriele at this time. A suppressed intensity about the eyes and the mouth, both sensuous, that an unsubtle observer would miss. If her simple little suit was anything but expensive, she had an innate elegance and the long slender bones that would have triumphed over a much less ambitious garment. In any case, she had no intention of squandering what money had been left to her. She was nineteen years old, half way through her Art Degree. After that she would teach and the rest of her studies would be done at night.

The mention of her aunt's name seemed to have changed everything, for the girl in the dashing tailored uniform had turned from pleasant, professional indifference to complete, unswerving attention. For a moment, a moment only, mind! she dropped into the vacant seat beside Gabriele, lowering her voice to a friendly conspiratorial aside. 'And to top everything, *Paul Lynnton.* I mean he's divine, isn't he? A gorgeous guy!'

'I've never seen him!' Gabriele confessed rather dryly, shades of her father's style, and for an instant the other girl transferred her stare into space as though the unwelcome suspicion crossed her mind that she was being taken for a ride. 'You've never seen him?'

'No, nor my Aunt Camilla. This will be my first visit to Sundown.'

'You lucky, *lucky* devil!' the air hostess said feelingly, rolling up her expressive eyes. Privately she was of the opinion that the undoubtedly chaste ice maiden beside her would melt in such a setting. The parties, that magnificent home, the wonderful clothes and *the men!* All of them filthy rich! 'Listen, honey!' she said patiently, an adult to a child. 'Make the most of it. I can see at a glance that you haven't your aunt's fabled resources. I guess all of us have a rich relative some place, so don't take offence. I tell you *I* wouldn't take a chance like that lightly. If I were you, I'd get into Adelaide, buy yourself a few new clothes, something with a swing. It might clean you out, but it will be well worth it in the long run. You've got lovely legs, but your skirt is too long. *Mrs. Paul Lynnton!* Why, honey, she only mixes with the best!'

The limpid grey eyes seemed far away, a little amused perhaps, certainly unimpressed, so that the older girl rose to her feet with a kind of friendly contempt, quick to lose interest. There was no justice anywhere, she thought with some envy. Now *she*, given the chance and the money, would bloom like grapes on a vine, while this pale, aloof creature, with a profile right out of an old-fashioned legend, merely looked thoughtful, introverted, her uncanny eyes searching out motives to the very heart. Everyone knew it didn't pay to ask too many questions of life. There were no answers in any case.

With a series of quick, little up-and-down movements of her fingers, the air hostess waved goodbye, leaving Gabriele with the impression that she had been found decidedly wanting, like a bad actress about to mess up a wonderful part. The part of a lifetime. Now with Mamma and her incredibly dear father gone, she couldn't care less. If someone had suddenly got up in front of her and announced that the plane was going down, she would have taken it with enormous calm. Love made the world go round. Love of one's own. Her Aunt Camilla was the favoured one. Or was she? For however short a time they had, her mother and father had been supremely happy. She must always remember that.

The conversation with the air hostess had been revealing. It was clear that she would gladly have swapped places with Gabriele any day. Different things were important to different people, Gabriele rightly supposed. She cared nothing now for Sundown, or indeed anything most girls of her age dreamed about. All she wanted was her parents back. All she had to accept with dumb resignation was that she was on her own. But Mamma's face, her sweet voice, her lovely vivacity, would always endure. She had only to look in the mirror to see her father reflected there. Nature had provided an ever-constant reminder—the same bones, the same colouring, the same cool reserve. The same strong loyalties and deep vein of humour, but only one's friends and one's loved ones ever really came to see that. She was a quiet girl. Not quiet in the sense that she had nothing to say, for she was an excellent conversationalist, as her father had been, when the subject had meaning, but rather, she had no great aptitude for inconsequential chatter. Far more of a *must*, that one would have supposed. The air hostess's extravagant dismay had been quite genuine. In fact, if a job had hung on Gabriele's personality and appearance she would have missed it. Mamma would have laughed at that. Would Aunt Camilla?

She couldn't have been kinder, nicer, when Gabriele, choking back the tears, had rung her. The distress and grief in the sweet voice, so like Mamma's, had been evident even over the long distance. She had been ill at the time—some dreadful virus. She couldn't come, but Gabriele must come to her, when it was all over. Did she need money? *No, just someone, some relative, who had known and loved Mamma and Father*. The sweetly imperious voice had quickly closed the gap . . . 'When it's all over, promise me now, Gabby, you'll come to me. My own niece, and to think I've never laid eyes on you. Paula really should have brought you down to us—but we can't talk about that. You sound so . . . *strange*, darling, in any case. A wee bit bottled up, like your dear father, but I know how you feel. Just come to me and I'll help you all I can. You can't imagine how stricken I am by this dreadful news!' No more stricken than I am, Gabriele had thought, and just as quickly chided herself for her odd, unwarranted reaction. There were real tears in that golden voice.

The strange part was, even after that long-distance phone call Gabriele might never have followed up her aunt's invitation, being oddly sensitive on that score, but for the letter. It was typed, to be sure, Aunt Camilla had probably dictated it to her secretary or whatever, and forgotten to sign it, but it was so warm and sincere, so much what her sore, nineteen-year-old heart wanted to hear, she couldn't have refused such a gracious plea. Almost as if Aunt Camilla wanted to make up for the long years apart. For the first time in her life Gabriele had felt an eager rush of love for this aunt she had never seen. She was Mamma's sister, which meant that for all her hectic social life and purported lavish spending she was a very real person, with Mamma's heart and depth of understanding. The letter proved it. Aunt Camilla, at last, was no shadow figure but a woman of flesh and

14

blood. Her *own* flesh and blood. She would love her. That hard knot of pain, that dreadful sense of loss, for the first time in many long months seemed to ease.

At the airport, unexpectedly, she was met by a very pleasant young man, almost as fair as herself, medium height and very well dressed—Noel Danton. He was also very efficient, for in no time at all he had a porter, her baggage, and they were seated in his car, very much what she expected, moving with precision through the long lines of traffic on their way to his home in one of Adelaide's loveliest suburbs, famous for its avenues of graceful colonial sandstone houses set in wonderful leafy gardens. It was often said of Adelaide, capital of the State of South Australia and Australia's cultural heart, that a great deal depended on whether one went to *that* school or married into *that* family, and Gabriele was to find in a short time that to a large degree this was true. Certainly so far as Noel Danton was concerned no further recommendation than that she was Camilla Lynnton's niece was needed. Acutely perceptive, Gabriele had the feeling had she been as plain as a barnyard fowl Noel (they were on first name terms already) wouldn't have changed his style, which was warmly admiring. The Lynnton name provided all the plumage that was needed and Noel was, in fact, a Lynnton employee, an up-and-coming executive, to be sure, though he freely admitted, charmingly taking Gabriele into his confidence, that he found the Terrible Old Man awesome, as hated as he was brilliant and totally in his old age unapproachable except for one person, and Gabriele at that stage was not sufficiently interested to ask who, assuming as she did that it would be his grandson, Aunt Camilla's husband, Paul Lynnton.

15

'Kyle is coming in to pick you up.'

'I beg your pardon!' Her expression changed immediately. She really would have to stop this way she had of withdrawing. Living with her thought crowded past.

'Kyle. Kyle Tyson!' Noel repeated in his cultured drawl, taking in his passenger's innocence at a glance. 'I'll tell you before the others do, some say he's the Old Man's son!' His laugh was cynical. 'Illegitimate or not, Tyson's got the whole town eating out of his hand—a chip off the old block. That should prove it if nothing else does. Even Camilla ...' Almost too late his sense of discretion came back to him. 'But that's all hearsay, as the law men say. Wait until you meet him and judge for yourself.' It was the worst possible line he could have taken with Gabriele, who was scrupulously fair. She raised her cool as rain grey eyes straight into his, making him with all his personal accomplishments and his business triumphs for the moment uneasy. 'Mr. Tyson is?' she enquired in her lovely low voice.

'Sir Joshua's right-hand man. All he *will* admit to. Tyson's mother was Rachael King before her marriage. You know the King family, of course?'

'I'm afraid not,' Gabriele said calmly. 'Unless they're the pioneering family. Cattle?'

'The same ones! It's no secret that old Josh went to pieces when Rachael Tyson died. That was about ten years ago. Tyson has been in the firm ever since.'

There was not a breath of curiosity in Gabriele's voice. 'I'm sure if Sir Joshua lives up to his formidable reputation, Mr. Tyson is more than adequate to the demands of the position.'

'Oh, he's *that*.' Even to Noel's own ears, his voice sounded thin, ultra-sarcastic. 'Enter the wily fox, as adroit as they come. He's a rare bird, our Tyson. Ruthless and charming when it suits him, a Machiavelli with style!'

'You don't like him?' Gabriele asked, her grey eyes reflective, and Noel laughed again, his senses aroused despite himself by the sun on her hair. 'Gabriele,' he said lightly, dwelling on her name, 'Kyle Tyson is not a man one likes! Men, women, either go all the way with him or hate him. He's a very complex type altogether, lots of charisma, but he does have the ability to attract the best people to him.'

'Socially, in a business sense, what?'

'Socially. Business-wise. Politically. You name it. Tyson can mastermind any intrigue and what's more, carry it off. The Old Man is eighty-four now. Tyson is practically running the show.'

This time Gabriele didn't look at him; her eyes were on the silver ribbon of river. 'And what of my uncle? Paul Lynnton. Surely, as Sir Joshua's grandson ...?'

Noel made a soft, clicking noise. 'So many things you *don't* know. Tell me, where have you been all your life, angel?'

The nickname which she was to become used to was typical of Noel. She faintly tilted her head, her eyes crystal clear as though she saw too much. 'It would seem in business,' she said gently, 'that it's the done thing to cut one another's throats. Yet I thought you were in the same team?'

A crow of ironic laughter answered her. 'Team! God, that's a good one! No one has ever seen Tyson run in harness. From the first day he started he pulled rank on all of us. It was like an invasion. The old warhorse with all his young vigour. I tell you it was uncanny. A man of iron habit, Tyson, and a real loner!'

'Then one person at least I shall recognise' she said

17

with sweet solemnity. 'I'm something of a loner my-self.'

Malice was hardly concealed in the smooth, good-looking face turned to her. 'You're as likely to have as much in common with Tyson as Lucifer himself. Though he too was an angel, now that I recall!' Almost for a moment Noel actively disliked her. She was watching him with intelligence and judgment, but by nature and control there was little he could learn from her face. It was an unforgettable sort of face, he thought with surprise in his own observation, yet she hadn't the sort of look he favoured. She was much too grave, with no attempt at any sort of artifice. She was too natural—a strange girl like a figurine cool as alabaster. Sunlight lacquered the pearly skin and sent shivering streams of gem stones through her silver-gilt hair. Her suit a champagne colour, Camilla, or indeed any woman in his immediate circle, wouldn't be caught dead in, yet long slender legs, irreproachable, flowered out of the discreet length of the skirt. His gaze, deliberate and professional, for he considered himself something of a connoisseur of women, was more than ordinarily intense, so that for the first time Gabriele smiled, lifting the faintly haunted look from her face, leaving it young, crystal-fresh.

The quick intake of his breath was audible. 'When you smile like that, you're an entirely different person!'

'Not at all! You don't know me—a more likely explanation.'

'Well, I think you can manage to relax a bit now. Stop worrying and start living!' The element of shock came back to him, like an echo in his own voice. 'You know, you're a really beautiful girl. I never noticed before.'

Gabriele gave him a faintly amused look and let the observation lapse into silence. Noel, at once and for ever, would have little influence on her, yet it would take him a long time to realise this, cocooned as he was in what passed for self-confidence, but what was really an extremely thick hide.

She put up a slender, ivory-smooth arm and brushed back her hair, anxious to steer the conversation away from the personal. 'It's very kind of Mr. Tyson to pick me up in any case.'

'Anything to help Camilla out!' Noel volunteered with heavy nuance, not in the least put out by her disinclination to play the usual games.

'You seem to trust in my discretion, Mr. Danton,' she said lightly, 'or you like to be candid in public. Either way, it can be dangerous, surely?'

'Not with eyes like yours,' he said blandly. 'Don't underestimate me either, angel face. I'm a fair judge of who has a taste for intrigue. In any case, a lordling like Tyson would hardly be troubled by my opinion!'

And small wonder! Gabriele thought with an unaccustomed little burst of antagonism. Noel's remarks she considered to be both improper and indefensible, but equally well she knew he would only think her overly fastidious. Fastidious or not, she didn't care for this character assassination and she wished he would stop. Far from stopping, he was still saying:

'You'll find out, Gabriele angel, that Tyson's not human, but a machine with all a machine's iron certainties. And something else, but I don't know what it is.'

'It sounds a little as if you might desire it for yourself!'

He burst into his light, saturnine laugh. 'There's more to you than I would have thought. In fact, my lady, you look me through and through. But I don't mind telling you that from you I've decided to swallow snubs and insults galore!'

The cruising car slowed and turned into a wide street lined with beautiful shade trees. The houses were set well back in their rambling grounds, none of them modern or super-sophisticated but mellow and gracious like a self-assured dowager from a bygone era. The instant before Noel swung off the road into a broad, pebbled drive, Gabriele looked towards him and smiled:

'Your home?'

'Right in one. It's been in my mother's family for a long, long time. Dad more or less had to live here!'

'No hardship!' Gabriele decided, her eyes on the house, 'unless he had a decided mind of his own!'

'He hadn't!' Noel murmured dryly, 'or if he did, he was brainwashed well in advance. Denise will keep us company until Tyson arrives.'

'Denise?'

'My mother,' said Noel. 'I haven't called her that since I was about ten. Probably before then. I was at boarding school most of the time, just down the road. My mother is one of the new wave of women, gallant ladies, who rejoice in the fact that they never show their age, much less discuss it. I recommend you to call her Denise right from the start. She doesn't like Mrs. Danton either. Never did!' Noel's voice was bantering, but it had a faint uncomfortable edge, and Gabriele, really looking at him for the first time, realised that Noel, too, was older than she had supposed. Had she been asked she would have put his age at perhaps twenty-nine, and then she would have been a good five years out.

He could feel her eyes watching him and he turned his head towards her a moment and smiled. 'Nothing is as it appears to be. Remember that, angel, it's the key! Look long and hard at the scenes played out for your benefit. Advice from a friend, and that's what I want to be. Now, we're here. I'll get someone to bring your gear up.'

Inside the house, with its urban elegance, Noel was greeted by an uncompromisingly plain but competent-looking woman who opened a door at the far end of the hall and hurried towards them.

'You're back, Mr. Danton, and Miss Somerville!' Blue, very shrewd eyes ran over Gabriele, like a room that needed attention. Both women exchanged conventional smiles.

'Hello there, Jo!' Noel acknowledged lightly, rather offhand. 'Is my mother about?'

'Resting upstairs. I understand there is a party tonight.'

'This is Mrs. Josephsen,' Noel said with a vague sketch of his hand. 'Our housekeeper and the leading Cordon Bleu in this town, except for Camilla's. Call my mother, would you, please, Jo, and tell her we're here. I want her to meet Gabriele.' Without looking back, Noel gestured Gabriele into the large room opening off the hallway. 'Come in, angel, and make yourself comfortable. You might have a long wait. It's impossible to pin Tyson down to time and place.'

'That's not true, Noel, and you know it!'

A slight fair woman, immaculately turned out, with her son's neat, regular features and bright hazel eyes slipped into the room by another route, surprising both of its occupants. Noel spun around and gave a faintly ironic shrug. 'My mother is yet another of Tyson's fans!'

'And you know exactly why!' Denise Danton's hazel eyes met Gabriele's without the slightest trace of welcome or good humour, but very searching, missing not one detail of the composite picture.

'And you're Paula's daughter?' She held out her small white hand and Gabriele took it, asking in turn her own question. 'You knew my mother?'

'My dear girl!' Denise Danton said lightly, 'everyone knew the beautiful Lawrence girls, yet you have no look of your mother. Camilla either, which is to say the same thing. Perhaps fortunate! It wouldn't do for Camilla Lynnton to have a younger version of herself around.'

Noel's drawling voice cut across his mother's. 'Do let's sit down. Have a drink. Anything!' He moved over to a beautiful carved cabinet that housed a whole collection of the best labels, but his mother had a better idea.

'I imagine Gabriele might like to freshen up after that long trip, but find yourself a drink by all means!' She let her eyes wander away from her son's, seemingly totally disinterested, and beckoned to Gabriele. 'Come along, my dear, and I'll show you where.'

Moving lightly, she led the way to a small room on the opposite side of the hallway and ushered Gabriele into the rather luxurious privacy, yellow, gold and white, of the downstairs powder room and almost immediately left with the specific caution : 'It pays to take time!'

Gabriele caught sight of her own rather startled reflection and decided she liked it immensely. At least it had some sort of serenity. The Dantons appeared to be aflame with hidden grievances. There was a very forced air of good humour about Noel's banter and Gabriele fancied she detected in Mrs. Danton a faint note of hysteria. At any rate the atmosphere in this lovely home was far from festive. With something of her old whimsicality, she gave her face her undivided attention. She knew without a doubt that Mrs. Danton would regard several hours a day at this kind of thing as perfectly natural, sandwiched in between luncheons and parties. Prisoners, her mother used to call self-obsessed ladies, buried up to their necks in renewal and revival kits. For the next ten minutes she broke all her own records in completely re-doing her make-up, and emerged looking pretty well the same as when she went in, her hair a gleaming curtain about her small head.

Her footsteps on the thick carpet were noiseless and she might have wished for parquet, for, disturbed and embarrassed, she was the unwilling witness to the soft, clashing sound of voices. Mother and son, each showing their tensions in the same way. Comical really if their complaints weren't so deadly. This was nothing like home, the wonderful, loving, mutually considerate home she had known. Grief made her suddenly and uncontrollably sick of the whole thing. Should she give a hoarse, theatrical cough, or just barge right in, seeing she was the object of the discussion? In one detail only did the Dantons agree; it seemed she could not be expected to enjoy her sojourn at Sundown. If she hesitated another minute, perhaps she would find out why.

With a graceful, avid glance into the hallway, Noel chanced to catch sight of her fascinated profile in the giltwood mirror that hung above the stairs. 'We're in here!' he called out with his effortless irrelevance, and Gabriele judged it safe to walk on.

'Beautiful! Bellissima! You look marvellous!' he said, and turned to regard Gabriele inquisitively, his fingers laced across his finely striped shirt.

Mrs. Danton in a room full of formal furniture was now seated in a light-scale piece specially designed to complement her fragility, her hazel eyes bright and restless as though she had a headache behind them. 'You really overdo that type of thing, darling. Too much effervescence. Watch Kyle and learn a few things.'

'No doubt!'

'You know, you would really pay for dressing,' Mrs.

Danton suddenly observed, transferring her attention to Gabriele at the earliest possible opportunity. 'Your aunt certainly makes the most of herself, no one better. You might be said to be an opposite type, an exponent of the natural look. Of course, when one is as young as you are, with such flawless skin, it involves nothing, simply nothing to look good. I was ravishing as a girl!'

'Strange, I've heard no one else say that!' Noel remarked with a funny little grin, 'but Gabriele, now, finished, could look sensational!'

'Better delay the change, then!' Denise Danton suggested with cool obscurity, and looked towards Gabriele as if to test her reaction. She got none; in fact, Gabriele was calmly considering finding her own way to Sundown, but how could she when the arrangements had been made? It said something for Noel that he immediately grasped the trend of her thoughts, for he gave her a charming, conciliatory smile and walked over to her to put a small dry sherry in her hand. 'Sit down, Gabriele, and relax a while. Tyson has rung, as it happens. He should be along shortly. Camilla won't be at home this evening.'

'No, she'll go on to the party!' Denise Danton cut in adroitly. 'The same one I'm going to myself. None of our really big occasions are complete without Camilla!'

'You look a little tired, my dear,' Noel informed his mother without any emotional inflection at all. 'I can only think you've been gadding about too much of late!'

'And if I have ...' Mrs. Danton started up with a flurry.

Gabriele tilted her head and sipped at her drink, finding the Dantons staggeringly candid. Much better to be remote or mysterious than let one's instincts to attack go unimpeded.

The chimes on the front door throbbed through the house, awakening mother and son rather drastically. Noel jumped to his feet, setting his glass down so firmly that the frail stem was threatened, while his mother entered vividly into a new dimension. Showing a truly unusual burst of initiative, she was already borne off on her small feet as if by a strong current. 'That will be Kyle!' Her voice floated back to them, so gay, so infused with feminine excitement that Gabriele almost laughed. 'Kyle! Punctual to the minute. You made that in galloping time!'

Noel was still standing, unaccountably without his usual, self-possession, transfixed, hanging as anxiously as his mother on the answer. For the first time in many long months Gabriele became more than a saddened observer. She was actually participating in this decidedly odd scene, unable to prevent herself looking towards the hallway.

A man's voice answered immediately, so vibrant and alive that Gabriele found herself tensing in the high wing-backed chair, sitting straighter, framed within its brocade sides like a princess in thrall. She never actually heard his amusing response, she only knew she had crossed a new frontier. They came in at once. The woman, with her bright hazel eyes and strange sea change. The man ... Noel's fallen angel, Lucifer. She could see why he had used the metaphor. Kyle Tyson carried with him a wonderfully lucid air of authority. An uncontrived power, thunderously alive. Black-haired, teak-polished skin tailored very exactly over definite bones, glinting eyes, with the startling sheen of Florentine silver. Taller than most, with a corresponding breadth of shoulder, he conveyed instantaneously a dynamic and individual personality. It was easy to ap-

25

preciate that he could in different moments and moods be taken for awesome, brilliant, ruthless, a man's man to be followed with unswerving allegiance; to a woman ... what? ... as unlikely to be chained as forgotten.

He looked towards Gabriele with the straight lancing look she was to become familiar with, and curiously she recognised that for all his remarkable aura he was neither strange nor hostile to her as the Dantons were. Simply, he knew her, as though a glance was sufficient for him to interpret her whole personality. Noel was shaking his hand, talking with a great many exclamation points, attentive and nervous, and Gabriele observed in silence the rather splendid courteous insolence with which the light gaze passed from Noel to his mother and on to her. A royal kind of indolence. Lucifer!

Denise Danton was bubbling and gesturing with her small, bejewelled hand. 'This is Camilla's niece. You'd never pick her, would you?'

'No!' Conviction threaded the decisive voice. 'How are you, Gabriele? A beautiful name, and you're much too young for Miss Somerville.'

She gave him her hand, raising her grave eyes to him. 'How do you do, Mr. Tyson.'

He looked down at her, the ghost of a smile flickering about his well-defined mouth, the easy, restrained strength of his hand offering some reassurance that at much puzzled as comforted her. 'If you're ready, I'd like to get back to Sundown.'

Denise Danton gasped her dismay, her bright hazel eyes gazing up at him as if he were the fount of truth and male beauty, in reality myopic, the desperately needed glasses on these occasions discarded. 'Surely you'll stay a few moments, Kyle?'

'Not tonight, thank you, Denise!'

26

She laid a hand on his arm, as if her disappointment might swing the scales, her face above the beautiful dress unexpectedly young with its full quota of sleep and avoidance of alcohol, but in vain. 'Then we won't see you at the party?'

'No!' he said smoothly, conveying with artistry his regret. 'Some details that need tying up.' The strange eyes, almost incandescent, rested on Gabriele again, with her pearl-coloured skin, but now it was Noel's turn.

'But I was hoping to have a word with you about Price,' he jumped in with his marvellous facility for back-stabbing. 'I'm truly worried about him.'

'Not tonight, Noel!' Tyson repeated in a very calm, immovable tone, an indisputable top dog in a world full of underdogs. It was obvious that Noel thought as much; his expression fell into lines of sulky dignity which darkened as Tyson continued for his own reasons:

'Actually Ray may rush his fences a bit, but I'm inclined to think he's set on the high road to success. Few of the staff work harder.'

Denise Danton riveted a ferocious face on her son which he missed, becoming more noticeably upset, leaning stiffly against the mantelpiece. 'Well, there's no thrill like the thrill of big business,' he contributed at last. 'I don't trust him myself. All those tactical proposals!'

Tyson, after a very long day, kept his mind on the other man with an effort, well aware whether one was there or not, was an enormous telling factor in Noel's behaviour. 'I should if I were you,' he said lightly, but enough. 'The primary law of success is, as you know, drive and initiative. In any case Ray was thoroughly checked out before he joined the organisation.' He

27

glanced briefly at the sunburst clock. 'Now, Gabriele, if you're ready, it's rather a long drive back and I have to see Sir Joshua tonight. If you see me in the morning, Noel, some time after eleven, I'll brief you in detail.'

'Good show! I'd really appreciate that!' Noel exclaimed earnestly, diabolically two-faced just as his mother had come to the conclusion that he was amazingly stupid like his father.

'How is the old man?' she asked brightly, very wisely bowing to Tyson's inevitable departure. 'We see so little of him these days.'

'As unquenchable as ever! One might wish he'd slow down for his own sake, but I don't think he ever will. The prime factor in his being so remarkable, I suppose!'

Noel reached for a cigarette from an ivory box and lit it and Gabriele realised she was watching a parlour game, the whole of her brain given over to it. Only Kyle Tyson's presence made it all life-size, his dynamic aura an extension of his tall, powerful frame. She could sense in Noel that feeling of constraint masked by a professional friendliness. Fundamentally the two men could never be friends or even compatible, for there was on Noel's part a basic antipathy towards the stronger, surer, more brilliant man who could outflank and manoeuvre at every turn, and who moreover appeared to show no shame in his uncertain origin. Noel himself had great pride in his own. His mother's people had been among the colony's earliest, influential settlers. It would have crippled Noel entirely, and even then Gabriele guessed it; Kyle Tyson thought of him as little more than an advanced schoolboy, valuable in public relations where he put up a good front, but beyond that requiring the drawing of diagrams.

'I'll get Gabriele's luggage into the car!' Noel volunteered helpfully, lifting himself clear out of his depression and went on ahead while his mother escorted her favourite visitor to the door. Gabriele fell back a few respectful paces, content to let her eyes rest on a sculptured dark head inclined with a gallant but incurious humour towards the small Dresden figure at his side, unaccountably come alive. At the door the shrewd hazel eyes turned faintly melancholic. Denise Danton was now after many years, mostly dreary, a widow, but the birthdays, the birthdays!—and this superb man was too young. Still, she was one of the charmed circle around him, a wonderfully enriching experience. It paid to be one of Camilla Lynnton's best friends. Camilla so flamboyantly beautiful with her magical look of youth that went on for ever and ever. If only she could be Camilla, if only for a night! The women who vied for his attentions in any terms of profit were legion, but mostly unlucky. Except Camilla. There, as Camilla wordlessly implied, as in the vicious bitter world of big business he had talent amounting to genius. A much less feminine woman than Denise Danton would have known it with great certainty.

Gabriele, very young and inexperienced, only knew that in some indefinable way she was drawn to him. Perhaps it was the cool, level approach, the lurking of humour that reminded her of her father. Yet in no other way could she see any resemblance. Her father, for instance, would not have survived in Kyle Tyson's world. Kyle Tyson with his enormous expertise in handling people and problems. Who or whatever he was, he was the real thing. No apologies to anyone. Clever and powerful, he probably knew without illusions that he was all of those things.

Her sweetly phrased farewells over, Denise Danton

transferred her attention to Gabriele, frowning in that first instant, as if she had received a good many unfavourable impressions. 'So nice to have met you, my dear,' she said graciously, tilting her head to the slender young girl. 'I won't say goodbye, as of course I'll be seeing a great deal more of you. Camilla is one of my dearest friends!'

Gabriele came up with a polite response, taking *that* statement with a surprisingly straight face. It was difficult to judge friendship when loyalty was so astonishingly unreliable. Noel, not to be left out, now joined them at the side of the car, lifting Gabriele's hand to his lips, a gesture he carried off with truly Gallic flair and very little practice. 'Dinner one night soon!' he murmured *sotto voce*, conveying an unwarranted degree of intimacy. 'I'll ring!' He held the door for her while she slipped into the passenger seat. 'I hope you'll be comfortable in there,' he said with a facetious smile, the car matching its owner in its splendid mien. Across the sleek bonnet he could see his mother still clutching Kyle Tyson by the wrist as if she was clay in his hands and he lifted his head and gave in to the unforgivable:

'Mother!'

In this, the most rigorous test of her mature self-control, Denise was quickly restored to order. She stood back from the car with a polished smile: 'Until we meet again!' dipping her faultlessly arranged head to give Gabriele a last frosty smile as though she bitterly envied the girl the trip to Sundown. Which she did.

Inside the car, going into an immaculate U-turn, Kyle Tyson suddenly gave a low, disturbingly attractive laugh in his throat. Gabriele looked swiftly at his dark profile, but he only turned his head full on and smiled at her without making a verbal contribution, his teeth very white against his tanned skin. The smile became reflected in her luminous eyes which counted a lot in terms of communication. Whatever this man was to become to her, friend or enemy, she would never have to explain herself to him. He had great skill as an interpreter.

CHAPTER TWO

OUT on the highway, they went like the wind. Only then did he flicker her another glance as though, hitherto, he had been wrapped in the cloak of his own deliberations.

'Tell me about yourself, Gabriele!'

'Do I have to?'

'Yes!' Another of his inexorable decisions. 'You may not get the opportunity again. Besides, doesn't it occur to you that I might really want to hear? I seldom waste time on fraudulent activities.'

'Or ever discount information from whatever the source,' she said with young irony, earning herself a silvery, sidelong look. 'But if you think it's the perfect opportunity, Mr. Tyson ...?'

'Go ahead. I want to hear you talk for quite a while yet. I have the feeling you'll lose a lot of that fine-drawn tension if you do. You're too young to carry all your burdens.'

'You may fall asleep in the first five minutes!' she cautioned, trying to summon up the moral courage to resist him.

'I promise not to drift off until you finish. Talk to me, little one, I'll follow every word!'

She didn't speak for another few minutes, under the spell of his influence, her grey eyes enormous, unblinking, not empty, but filled with aching complexities. She didn't know this man. She didn't need pity or charity or whatever it was he proposed to give.

'Gabriele!' he said in a voice of such affinity that she trembled, the tears threatening to spill. He was a monstrously attractive man with the uncomfortable gift of divining one's thoughts. She turned her head fleetingly, not knowing she looked like a solitary child, brave and forlorn, but the glance she got back left her so efficiently shaken that she began to speak, the tone of her voice, the quality of her gaze altering, the words coming out, softly intense, starting with the halcyon days of her childhood, the joyful planned trips to Sundown, the day-to-day serene content of her home life, right down to the vulnerable point in her heart, the empty world she found herself in without her beloved mother and father. It was, as he said, an enormous burden, not unique, but often insupportable for all that. Yet why should she tell this man, this dark stranger, every thought of her heart? Whatever the reason, she did, and even when later, her trust was sorely tried, she did not regret it.

From time to time as she talked he turned his face to her and saw the absolute clarity of her skin, the planes and shadows, the flawlessly moulded hollows. He had forgotten just how breathtaking a young girl could be. Finally she put up a hand and pushed back her hair, a gesture of exhaustion, a little confused by her own surrender to the sympathy of the man and the moment. 'I never thought to say quite as much as that. A certain amount of my secrets are now lost to me for ever!'

'Does it pain you?' he asked unexpectedly.

'No, not at all. And you, no doubt, are the reason. You're a very unusual man!' She stared down at her pale, slender fingers. 'And clever!'

'Be my friend, Gabriele,' he said soberly. 'You'll get nowhere crossing swords with me. In any case, your every confidence is safe with me, as I think you're well aware. Try to remember, as Tennyson, I think it was, said: Though much is taken, much abides. You're very

33

young yet, it's easy I know to praise stoicism, but your life will come right again.'

'I'd like to think so,' she managed with a little shuddering breath. 'I won't bother you again.'

'I hope you do, because I won't leave you alone until I see a great improvement. A nuisance, I know, when one is as reserved as you are, but there you are, that's the way I am!'

The warm gold dust of late afternoon was fading, giving way to the delicate, complex colours of dusk. The stillness was pierced by a sudden shaft of birdsong and Gabriele gave the sky her reverent attention, wrapped in her own little cloud of felicity that only the perceptions of the man beside her had created. But she was too young to think about that. Kyle Tyson dwelt in a world a Titan's leap away from her own, for all she was on the brink of an unknown adventure.

'Sundown!' She turned to him with soft urgency as though murmuring the name of a new star, her hair a silvery shimmer in the last rays of sunlight.

His glance brushed her own. 'It's a very beautiful house.'

'I know!' she said with great confidence. 'Mamma told me about it over and over, so much so that I can see it with clarity—the white house floating in a blazing green mist, the foothills, the vineyards, the grove of pine trees. The lake with the swans and the Grecian lady to feed the goldfish. I know I shall love it!'

'Well, houses are easy to love. Unlike people.'

Was there scorn in that startlingly light glance? She moved her head very slightly in a nervous, reflexive way. 'This isn't the moment of truth, is it? Because I feel at a decided disadvantage!'

'Just a moment, Gabriele, the suspense must be agonising, I know,' he bent his dark head and touched a flame to his cigarette. 'The fact is, I like you. A white dove in a gorgeous swarm of butterflies!'

'Then tell me what I want to know. I've told you so much about me. Aunt Camilla, Uncle Paul, the children, cousins I've never seen. Which parent do they resemble? My mother and Aunt Camilla might have been twins!' Recollection gave her face a pure and haunting beauty and looking towards her he gave a faint sigh.

She seemed oddly unaware of the degree of intimacy that had been established between them, rather disturbing had she considered it, and very skilfully and candidly accomplished, but even his enemies, loath to accord him any merit at all, would have said Kyle Tyson was very clever about people.

'The house has always been surrounded with such mystery for me,' she explained, her gaze shy and sensitive, at the same time prepared for anything life might offer or inflict. 'Mamma did that, of course, the mystique. She was quite lyrical about Sundown!'

'Your Aunt Camilla, you'll find, loves it with an absolute passion,' he smiled at her, feeling at the same time, faintly angry with all his unspoken knowledge. He had lost all memory of innocence, its crystalline sweetness. This child with her silvery, infinite fragility and the mark of stress on her touched some subterranean protective streak in him, one he had forgotten he had, much less called into use for many long years past—since his mother died, in fact. He didn't realise, absorbed in his own thoughts, that his face had taken on a very formidable cast, familiar to many, but not Gabriele. For a moment she felt lost in a labyrinth and a bright nerve began to tremble in her throat.

'What is it, child?' He turned on her in his dazzling

fashion and she gave him a swift unconsidered answer:

'You look rather as if you were considering throwing me to the lions. Imperious even, like a Roman Emperor!'

As he looked into her luminous, sea-eyes, an answer occurred to him immediately, but he never said it. His life had, and would remain, exclusive of schoolgirls. Instead he began to talk with great charm and authority about wine and the enjoyment of it: the world's great vineyards, all of which he had seen and sampled their produce without being able to enveigle a single secret. Sundown's home vineyard produced an excellent, rather austere and delicately flavoured dry red, one of the many, many fine wine-producing vineyards in South Australia, more than all the other States put together.

Thirty miles to the north-east lay the enchanting Barossa Valley, a beautiful river valley of orchards and vineyards and olive groves, not so very different from the Barrosa Valley in Spain after which it was named, if not so exactly ... 'The most important non-irrigated quality vineland in Australia,' Kyle Tyson pointed out. He inhaled on his cigarette and for an instant his face was illuminated by the tiny scarlet spurt of flame, his skin overlaid with a patina of bronze. 'When I find time,' he offered matter-of-factly, 'I'll take you on a tour of our best vineyards. Knowledge and pleasure served up on a silver platter!'

'That's very kind of you, Mr. Tyson,' she said, eyes and voice mysteriously soft.

'I know!' he confirmed with extreme gentleness and irony, one black brow shot up and he turned and gave her a faint smile. 'It's not my reputation. As a further mark of my favour, Gabriele, you may call me Kyle. I'm not, it has suddenly occurred to me, ready to become any young girl's medieval uncle!'

'I've not the slightest doubt about that!'

'In fact,' he added with a devastating twist of his mouth, 'if you promise to stop staring at me with those enormous gossamer eyes, I'll tell you something else. I had a slight but memorable acquaintance with your mother!'

'But you never said that before!' she exclaimed with considerable awe in her voice.

'Perhaps I've only just judged it the appropriate time.'

'I'm beginning to think you're some sort of a sorcerer,' she said with downcast lashes. It was a little difficult now to look at him.

'What man isn't?' he returned with a look she had to meet, so full of charm and faint cynicism, with a quality of sexual excitement new to her.

The grey eyes so unwillingly, it seemed, regarding him were like pools of quicksilver, he thought, his own glittering, alive with curiosity. Yet her beauty was that of a child, pure and passionless set in a patrician mould. Again he knew that sensation of protectiveness which, now, unaccountably acted as an irritant upon him. He concentrated on the road ahead, his voice more incisive than he actually intended.

'I was born in Adelaide, you know, although I spent a great deal of my childhood elsewhere. I met your mother through the simple expedient of bolting from one of my own mother's garden parties. I had a clear choice, either bolt or go mad, and I was always fairly enterprising. I literally ran your mother down and she sensed the avalanche too late. I was about twelve at the time and already type-cast as the gangling young oaf with a name for being excessively high-spirited. Your mother was more than generous to me. In fact, she was distinctly funny and compassionate—much too kind, for I'm sure

I must have hurt her. She was very petite, like Camilla. I recognised her, of course. Few people at that time didn't. The Beautiful Lawrence Girls, they were called in those days. I remember the incident quite exactly, the conversation between the schoolboy and the accepted young beauty. Your mother, it seemed, didn't like garden parties either—punitive affairs at the best of times, though Camilla regards them as among the supreme experiences of life, with perhaps an equal passion for parties!'

'You must know her very well.'

'Yes!'

She got his full attention then, his splendid dark arrogance set in its harshest mould, razor-sharp with a look of exceptional power. But it was not needed. Gabriele knew nothing of the burning social gossip, the misdeeds and the machinations accredited to him, far more than he had ever done. 'Please tell me more!' she begged him with that limpid look of innocence. 'You can understand, can't you, why I want to know more. Except for Aunt Camilla I have no one!'

The dark brow cleared in an instant. 'Listen, Gabriele,' he said briefly, her name on his lips unexpectedly beautiful. 'Learn a lesson and learn it well. You have yourself, always yourself, to fall back and rely on. An army of one. No promises, no excuses for anyone. Qualities of self-control and self-discipline you can strengthen with constant exercise. You're young yet, but there are qualities in you, probably far more than you realise, that will carry you safely through life. Your mother, I recall, had several distinguishing characteristics that set her apart from her more frivolous contemporaries—humour and grace, the blossoming compassion and tenderness which I'm sure you've inherited. You have no look of

her, yet I wasn't the least perplexed as to your identity!'
His eyes rested fleetingly on her. 'Your Aunt Camilla, on
the other hand, is a woman of considerable beauty,
great flair and ambition, who has produced with no ill
effects to her face or her figure, rather the reverse, two
handsome children for whom Sir Joshua has a fondness—
young Paul who is ten and Melissa about seven. They
will love you, I'm sure, but your Aunt Camilla, you may
find, has a different conception of life, of love perhaps,
than your mother, for all they were sisters with a striking superficial resemblance. Camilla has little interest in
domestic life as such, but she's a brilliant hostess, as she
has to be, and her house and garden and children are a
credit to her.'

'And her husband?'

Again the look of a drawn sword as quickly sheathed.
'You will meet Paul in due course. I've been told he's the
absolute antithesis of myself.'

'Is that good?' she asked delicately, knowing the first
sweet tingle of crossing him, but he only laughed.

'It depends on what's to be done and with what!' he
said with a kind of indolent alertness, the sparks in his
eyes blossoming. 'Paul has placed himself fair and
square in the lily field, but he's been thoroughly trained
in a hard school. We know one another's calibre at any
rate. He has an engaging sort of charm, Paul, that con-
tinually confounds me. Certainly there's a bond between
us.'

Aunt Camilla! For a dreadful minute Gabriele thought
she had said it aloud and her face registered her shock,
her eyes glowing a strange opal light. A grim pause
seemed to follow and she met it, recognising at a glance
he would make a frightening enemy. The last thing she
wanted.

'Oh, for God's sake, relax!' he said suddenly, reading her thoughts again. 'You're trembling!'

'I've stopped!' she said with an effort.

'You're tired. Put your head back.' It was said with the same dangerous air of command as a lion-tamer. 'If I'm driving too fast don't get perturbed. I know the road well. In any case, we'll make it. One piece of advice for you, little one—in the days ahead use your own judgment. It will serve you well. I haven't missed the intelligence, though you lack the wisdom of experience. Be yourself. Don't be made over. You're a copy of no one. An original!'

'But I won't be at Sundown long enough for any of that,' she said simply. 'I'll be returning home at the end of the vacation. I'm only half way towards my arts degree.'

'After which you'll ...?'

'Teach!'

Children and flowers had the same simplicity. 'We'll see!' he said.

It was like a whip cracking. Thrashed into compliance, Gabriele thought, and smiled. 'Why *we?*'

'I have a great deal of say, Gabriele!' He spoke with a kind of impatience as if he had no time to pretend.

'Not with me!'

He contrived to look acidly amused, his eyes startling under their strongly marked brows. 'What did I tell you! The first show of independence. Go to sleep. For all you know, I might find independence in a woman tiresome, let alone a girl child. Especially when they seem as frail and unsubstantial as the dawn wind.'

'But you can't know about that!' she pointed out gently, her chin not softly cleft for nothing.

He gave her a long narrow stare. 'Perhaps not. You

40

have something of value, Gabriele, I'll grant you that! Now we both need a respite. Close your eyes. Moonstones—has anyone told you that?'

'No, *Mr. Tyson.*'

'You're not lacking in bravery, then?' Beneath her closed eyelids she heard the smile in his voice. 'For better or worse, Gabriele, I fear I must meddle in your affairs.'

'Heaven protect me, then!' she said, and gave a soft little sigh.

'Seeing talk won't alter matters! Would you like that window up a bit?'

'No, thank you. The breeze is delicious.'

'You don't mind if I get whipped in the face with that jewelled mane?'

'Oh, I'm sorry. I really am.' She sat up quickly, looking closely at him, seeing that there was indeed a long, silver-gilt thread clinging high up to the dark cloth of his jacket. She made a funny jerky little movement of her hand like an incantation and lifted it off again.

'That's not a spell, is it?'

'I'm sorry!' she apologised again, rather at a loss.

'Because if it is, I don't mind. It could stay there for ever.'

She stared into his dark face with growing gravity, then abstractedly settled further into the plush upholstery, her head tilting backwards. It gave her a mingled sensation of infinite luxury and a strange loss of balance. After that she lapsed into silence, the evening air heavy with a sweet, fresh fragrance. The engine responded to the man's demands with a surge of power, leaping forward in the lavender dusk like some powerful beast.

The scenery, the isolated houses, the long patches of

vacant land, the wide open fields were held in the hushed breath of evening. After that she lost all sense of time. They were on an eternity of road that rose to the foothills. To Sundown.

CHAPTER THREE

SHE crossed from a light dreaming state with a traitorous reaction to the touch of a man's hand on the skin of her arm.

'Wake up, Gabriele! We're almost there.'

'I can't believe I was asleep!'

'Disconcerting to discover you have been. Perhaps not deeply, but almost there. Do you always give your subconscious an airing?'

'If I do, it's my misfortune, I'm sure! What did I say?'

'Classified information,' he retorted dryly, his eyes moving over her face. 'Don't worry, it was entirely innocent and emphatically worth hearing. I enjoy such easy, arrant nonsense!'

'Oh, don't tease me, please!' she said low-voiced.

'It's true. Really it is. Accept it without further question. I've never been able to deceive children. I'm not Lucifer, at any rate.'

'I couldn't have said that!' she murmured, feeling incredibly foolish.

'You *did*!' He threw her a shimmery, speculative glance. 'It makes one wonder if you shouldn't go easier on the ... sherry, wasn't it?'

'How extraordinary!' She folded her hand into a tight little fist and still found him watching her. 'You must have lived through some difficult moments.'

'Not at all! I've been called worse things, perhaps not so fanciful!'

'You'd be bound to!' she pointed out with some perception. 'You're very unusual!'

43

'How do you know?' he said in a voice that made her skin prickle. 'We've only just met. Tell me again in another year or so. Your opinion might change.'

'I suppose so, when there are so many things I don't know.'

'You're not alone in that, Gabriele, that's the trouble. I sometimes wonder if I've achieved anything at all these past years. That's a testimonial!'

She shook her head rather helplessly. 'A curious thing for a man in your position to say. Are you in earnest?'

'Yes.' He gave that elusive, extraordinarily attractive smile.

'Well, I don't understand!' She rested her chin on one closed hand. 'You're brilliant at your job, young to be so very successful. Your whole life is in front of you.'

'That applies as much to you as to me, Gabriele,' he pointed out dryly.

'Well, I should be very triumphant!'

'Would you, Gabriele?' he asked rather moodily. 'The world should be full of sweetness and light, but it's not. I've found it a jungle where only the ruthless survive!' He gave her a faint smile. 'Why look so troubled? If I'm talking like this, it's your fault. I think you'd find my way of life an undignified striving for unworthy ends, or you have that effect on me. The unwitting spark!'

'I don't think I deserve that!'

'Yes, it does make one wonder! Sweet Ophelia with flowers in her hair!' His downbent glance was sharp with amusement.

She studied him for a moment, her mind completely arrested, unaware that her grey eyes were as curious, as exploratory as his own. 'May I ask you a few questions about yourself?'

'No!' he said instantly, not a whit embarrassed. 'I'm

44

very secretive, Gabriele, and there's no use pretending otherwise.'

'I was only going to ask you about your childhood.'

'I know the sort of thing you'd ask,' he said idly, 'and all I will say is, it couldn't have been very much like your own.'

'I'm sorry. I had a very happy childhood.'

'And it's left its mark of serenity on you for all your great loss. No, I'd much rather talk about you.'

'I think you know now all there is to know. Very little really!'

'And much more than I deserve to know from the tone of your voice—very young and aggrieved. Forgive me, little one, but my closeness is notorious. So far as you're concerned, experience will come. I hope for you it will be all the right kind.'

She looked without focus out of the window. 'Didn't someone say all experience is good and bitter experience the best of all?'

'Voltaire. Typically gloomy, for all he knew what he was talking about. I wouldn't want too many hard knocks for you.'

'You must have a protective streak you don't often acknowledge, yet with the light from the dashboard, you look . . .'

'Ruthless?' he forestalled her, almost flippant.

'I wasn't going to say that!' she protested, genuinely shocked. Impervious, perhaps. Tricky as they come, but not ruthless. There was too much humour in the curve of the mouth.

'You don't have to!' he was saying sardonically. 'I've heard it before from your own sweet sex.'

'Don't slander us all,' she said with a little surge of spirit. 'We're not all the same!'

45

'Forgive the contradiction. I haven't much proof of your claim to date. Disillusionment induces a little wisdom—elegaic but true. Beautiful faces, for instance, are often a gross misrepresentation. It tends to make a man indignant or nervous according to his temperament.'

'Which are you?' she asked impishly, seeing his dark face amused.

'Bored, for the most part.'

'If I were you I'd feel very superior!'

'I do!' His light eyes lanced across to her. 'From the vantage point of my piled-up experience. Primitive emotions and all their fiendish complications! Whereas you, Gabriele, of the rain-coloured eyes, have a total ignorance of the subject, I feel.'

'And if I do, I can still see you wouldn't easily play into a woman's hands. It seems odd when you're so very attractive!'

She had never seen a smile like that before, so worldly, so mocking with a faint edge of surprise. 'Now that's what I call starting in harmony. Thank you, Gabriele, a compliment is always something to grip hard on. It was a compliment, I hope!'

'I always advocate friendliness, where possible, Mr. Tyson!'

'*Kyle!*' he said, with a mocking lilt. 'We'll keep it that way, if you don't mind. Part of my terms. Tell me, Gabriele, why do you disguise yourself as a quiet little thing?'

'I usually fit that category,' she said, brushing her hair from her eyes.

'Allow me to pursue the question. Why? It's perfectly plain at our first meeting that you're not!'

'I would have thought quiet described me fairly exactly,' she murmured, slanting her shining blonde head.

'It doesn't!' he said with dry tenacity. 'Beckoning, perhaps. You have that way about you.' The bold, handsome face was faintly sceptical. 'You're not a member of the fairy folk, are you? A princess, maybe. Damn!' he broke off as a small furry creature darted across the headlights to miraculous safety.

Gabriele laughed gently in her throat at his expression and he turned to her, his eyes brilliantly alert. 'I generally use the mildest word available, Gabriele. It's not my aim to shock young women!'

'That's very reassuring!' She glanced at him out of shimmering, amused eyes.

He held her gaze lightly, then turned his dark head. 'You have a lovely voice, Gabriele. A priceless asset in a woman since time immemorial!'

She could feel herself flush and she let the cloud of her hair cover her face. 'I seem to be using it more than usual.'

'Keep it that way!'

He sounded charmingly indulgent, not the ruthless tycoon at all. 'I don't believe you're Kyle Tyson at all!' she said in an odd little rush.

'I am!' His indolent glance mocked her. 'The ravening wolf that eats up the lambs—though I did engage in a certain amount of reckless idealism in my youth. Time has its revenge. Nowadays, I only admit to a mild arrogance of soul. I hope you're not dismayed!'

'A little wary now I know the truth. You don't believe love is a many-splendoured thing, Mr. Tyson ... I'm sorry, *Kyle*. It's pretty hard to remember you have so much presence.'

'Is that delicate irony I detect? The thing is, Gabriele, as a rule I never gratify a woman's curiosity, but *no*! A pretty phrase, I admit, used wholesale by our lady

47

novelists. There's a lot more safety in self-discipline than open season. I wouldn't care to see you, for example, finish up with several undesirable husbands. Most unsuitable!'

'And right out of my range!' she protested. 'My kind of life is worlds apart from that!'

'Perhaps those worlds might collide. Have you thought of that? They say opportunity is the big telling factor when it comes to virtue.' He looked back at her with controlled cynicism, tolerant, experienced and definitely amused.

She could feel a slow heat start at her toes. 'No wonder you go your own way,' she said piously. 'Must everyone else follow?'

He gave her a look of total attention, possibly the origin of her funny giddy feeling. 'One moment, little one, while my mind encompasses the meaning of those words. Actually, I think, you should get a slap for it, but I'll allow you the privilege of the very young and the very old and let you get away with it.'

The instinctive little movement she made away from him betrayed her confusion. 'I didn't offend you, did I? I'd hate to do that!'

He stared at her with absolutely no expression at all. 'Is it possible that there's even more dimension to you than I first thought?'

'I can't see the vaguest sign of it myself,' she said a little shakily. 'It's costing me a considerable effort trying to appear adult and dignified after my lapse into silly, articulate sleep.'

He gave a short laugh and relented. 'At least it makes a bond between us. I don't think you delude yourself, Gabriele. Neither do I. There's not a one of us who can't be hurt—a vast company. The trick is to close the door on it so no one will know. As someone else said; what we know of love is bitter, and what else do we know?'

'Oh, don't say that!' she said with gentle vehemence, her slight body turned towards him, her large, lake-coloured eyes almost too big for the pale oval of her face. Something about him cut into her new, raw sensitivity, dividing them yet linking them closer together. His expression had changed, hardened. It came to her on a bright, fearful current. He looked very dark and dangerous, which was her way of interpreting the faint sensual hostility that stirred in his face. Her voice broke a little. 'You don't look as though you like me!'

'You're a very beautiful girl, Gabriele, and intensely feminine. Let me be one of the first to tell you that. To like you is out of the question. Let's say I appreciate you. With the superficial polish on you, that will surely come, you'll have the soft, luminous beauty of a pearl, in striking contrast to Camilla, your Aunt Camilla's diamond brilliance. Whether that's good or not, I won't tell, but it's inevitable. You're not a fledgling version of Camilla at any rate. Once you get to Sundown you'll be caught up in a mad merry-go-round of parties and social events. You'll have to dress the part.'

'I've no wish to do that,' she said with spirited sincerity.

'That's all been taken care of. No one, but no one, my girl, lets Sir Joshua down.'

'But I fail to see ...'

'Precisely. Let me do the seeing for you. For a while anyway. Everything and everyone at Sundown is Sir Joshua's concern.'

'I've read about such people, but I've never really believed in them. You said something significant, everything before everyone, possessions before people, is that right?'

He listened to her with indulgent irony, shrugging his broad shoulders in not so amused recollection of things long dead. 'You're too intelligent, Gabriele. I can only tell you there's not a person alive who could satisfy Sir Joshua's human heart.'

'How sad!' she breathed. 'How very, very, sad.'

A strange look softened his sculptured, dark face. 'I'm afraid you're right. Correction, Gabriele, I like you enormously. A man might starve without a woman's compassion—an honest confession you may never hear again. I want you to promise me something, if you're ever in trouble, or ever need advice, you'll come to me.'

'I shall be all right, don't worry.'

'Promise me!' he said without hesitation.

'I don't understand you,' she said without any inhibitions at all. 'What is it you're trying to tell me? We're strangers, yet we're not strangers at all.'

'Some people identify immediately,' he pointed out with rather weary assurance. 'Am I to get your promise or not?'

'Of course. Perhaps I'm a fatalist, but I feel you'll have some influence on my immediate future.'

'That's not being a fatalist, Gabriele,' he observed, fleetingly sharp. 'That's sound common sense. In that, you're far from defective.'

Unaccountably he had withdrawn from her, leaving her with the oddest feeling that she had failed him—a general disenchantment. The splendidly arrogant profile was lit with faint exasperation. Of humour and indulgence there was now no trace. She had never expected to feel so deprived.

'Don't be angry with me,' she said in her clear, young

voice. 'Surely you aren't?'

'I've a streak of natural cruelty,' he said in a hard, purposeful voice.

'Well, I haven't!'

'Perhaps that's why I'm drawn to you.'

'The cat and the mouse?'

His white teeth shone in his dark face. 'That's life, Gabriele!'

'A fairly hysterical mouse!' she said, and her face came to life in a smile.

'At least you've spared me a stale, dull journey.'

'Presumably because I've such a charming disposition?'

'I can think of no other reason,' he taunted her lazily, 'unless it's that shining fall of hair. Always an influence.' His lean strong fingers gently nudged the wheel. 'At the next bend we leave the main road and start climbing. You'll see the vineyards first, fanning away to the foothills—one of our veteran vineyards, set to Cabernet Sauvignon and Shiraz for the most part. The high altitude and the higher rainfall accounts for the high quality of the grapes. Sundown presents two styles, as you probably know, the straight Cabernet and an excellent, more forward, Cabernet Shiraz version. Even the young wines are soft and full but still retaining the distinctive Sundown delicacy. The 1964 straight Cabernet was a beautiful wine, a fine example of what the home vineyard can do. Needless to say it's hard to come by.'

'I imagine you've laid down quite a supply?'

'I have!' he flickered a brief, mocking smile at her, 'but it's a pity to drink it. It can only improve with age.' As he was speaking, they left the main road turning off into gently wooded country.

'Soon we should see the lights from the house,' he said

conversationally. 'It stands quite alone, I think, an architectural gem.'

A flicker of pain crossed her face, like the flash of light in a mirror. She sat forward, her grey eyes held wide. 'Sweet Sundown, my mother always called it,' she said, and her voice was a little unsteady. 'For *her* sake, now, far more than my own, I intend to enjoy every moment of it.'

'And what used your father say?' he asked in a strangely meditative voice which caused her to turn to him in faint surprise.

'My father always took the droll view on everything,' she explained. 'He liked to tease my mother about her old family home and she liked to play up to him. It was a kind of pleasurable game between them and as I grew older I was allowed to join in. I suppose I shall never know such true marital passion, always supposing I do marry. My parents were blessed as few people are. I've seen enough, heard enough from my friends, to know marriage *can* be terrible. But my parents were intensely happy in one another's company, very generous, not only to one another, but to everyone—the secret, I suppose. My father always found my mother enchanting, I do know that. You could see it in his eyes. The tenderness, as though he couldn't bear to hurt her. My mother had the vivid personality you remember from just a brief meeting, while my father was cooler, quieter. They were perfect foils for one another.' Her breath caught a little and he glanced at her swiftly.

'You're very fortunate in your memories, Gabriele!'

'Memories, yes. But each morning I wake up knowing the worst is true. They're gone and I'm quite alone. I'm sorry if I sound heartbroken. I am!' Her soft, wide eyes were shadowed by her lashes.

'There's no need to offer an excuse. Why should you *not* be? We must all be allowed a proper time for our grief, yet we can't resent the knowledge that life is for the living. The young don't weep for ever. Survival depends on a certain amount of self-interest. It's necessary, I'm afraid, to shed our burdens, otherwise it's near impossible to walk on. At the moment you're full of accumulated strain. It will ease.'

'I'm not going to disintegrate at any rate!'

'No, Gabriele, *you* won't! A whole lot of things will happen to you yet. Allow yourself your days of adjustment and life will assume purpose and meaning again. Accept it from one much older and wiser.'

She could feel herself responding to the beautiful timbre of his voice, the undercurrent of personal experience she could recognise. For whatever reason, he was handling her very gently indeed. 'For being so very kind to me,' she said spontaneously, 'you have my friendship for life!'

His light eyes sprang to rapier-sharp appraisal and one black brow lifted a little. 'Why, thank you, Gabriele. I believe you mean that. Fairly or unfairly I intend to hold you to it. I usually live behind a mask, you know, but for you, for a little while I appear to have lifted the shutters!' He smiled at her, an odd crooked little smile that still had sweetness to it, and she felt his charm wash over her anew. Charm that was held in restraint for the most part, yet still powerful enough to reach out for her like a lick of flame. Nervously, in reaction, she looked down at her pale, narrow hands, twisting the fine jade and gold ring that had belonged to her mother. 'Love makes one so terribly vulnerable, doesn't it? Romantic love, though I've never experienced it, not even a silly crush. Familial love I *do* know, the fears and anxieties of

53

a mother for her child. My own lonely wilderness of bereavement. I suppose it's impossible to love without suffering.'

'A sadly self-evident fact! Perhaps that's why I follow the principle of non-involvement. Even affection can be a responsibility.'

'Yet you're trying to be kind to me, I know!'

'I could no more evade it than turn you loose in a rain forest,' he said rather strangely. 'For every end there is a beginning, Gabriele, and no possible going back.'

She wanted to look at him but thought *much better not!* For her, she knew beyond any possible doubt, Kyle Tyson had created new territory, faced as she was for the first time with an essentially personal man-woman confrontation, but the gulf between them, mentally and emotionally, was enormous. Her life had been simple, simply related. What of his? Even then before that summer of turmoil had unfolded she knew their meeting was crucial, a by-product of her own sensitivity. She sighed and arched her back into the plush upholstery with no intention of being provocative, but he was very conscious of her, the slight and graceful femininity. Indeed she seemed to him a girl as fragile as a camellia with her pale hair and matt white skin. She would never dream of hurting anyone she loved. The eyes and the mouth, that fine-drawn look of suppressed sensuousness both tender and touching, told of a capacity for love that could rock her whole life.

Gabriele sensed the stillness in him, the withdrawal she could not understand. Because of this, she fell silent and deliberately began to name off the botanical names of the trees and the shrubs to herself. A safety valve? That too, and the acknowledgement so early in their acquaintance that this man could hurt her. He glanced at her averted profile, almost in recognition.

'I think you'll prove very sensitive, Gabriele, especially with me. You mustn't mind what I say and do. Promise? You told me you're my friend!'

'That sounds like an ultimatum, but yes, I promise, if you want me to.' She didn't change her pose but stared back at him with her look of clear-eyed honesty, and he smiled.

'You must have been a very pretty child. No, *beautiful*, with two silvery pigtails over each shoulder tied with a ribbon.'

'It's not possible! I can't believe you know that much about me.'

'Camilla has a photograph of you and your mother somewhere up at the house. You haven't changed much, if at all. All white and gold, loved and sheltered.'

'Up until now.'

'None of us can hide from our own tragedies, Gabriele. The thing is to take hold of our lives with both hands. Do you think you can do it?'

'I hope so!' Tears came into her eyes as she said it and she made a great effort not to become over-emotional, the expression on her face, both sweet and sad, highly commendable when faced with the almost immediate prospect of seeing her mother's old family home, the beautiful estate of Sundown where she had been born. Sundown. Sweet Sundown. Just the way her mother had said it made Gabriele realise the power of emotion and nostalgia it evoked. *Home* was home, a very important word in every man, woman or child's vocabulary.

Kyle Tyson turned his dark profile towards her and she could see that the lines of communication were open once more. 'It will be natural enough for you, Gabriele, to feel a lift of the heart in the face of your loss. No one takes Sundown for granted!' Firmly he caught her wrist as if to infuse strength into her. 'This is part of your heritage too, and don't let anyone tell you any different. What's bred in the bone will out!' His face and his voice were hard and sure, his strange eyes brighter than silver, and they saw such a lot. Old memories pierced her heart, sensations so new she could not put a name to them. He smiled faintly at her little look of bewilderment, his dark face alight with humour and mockery. Sophisticated, worldly, with the easy, assured charm of a man who knew and understood women, she felt a little lost, no match for him at all at nineteen, almost twenty. Evidently he thought so too, for his face softened, losing the dark and dangerous look that was as unsettling as it was sharply exciting. Casually he released her imprisoned fingers, his light gaze calm and imperious.

'We're approaching the estate now. At the next bend we leave the main road and then you'll get your first view of the vineyards spreading out like a peacock's train down the slopes. The estate has been running at a considerable profit for some years now. Sir Joshua has poured many millions into his latest venture, the latest and most scientifically devised equipment, highly qualified staff. Sundown manages to hold its own among the other vineyards, although its output is considerably less. The Cabernet Sauvignon is notoriously "shy", but the spring rains have been adequate with no high winds and the grapes are plumping very nicely. A burst of hot weather and no storms and we should have a vintage year. Close to the house we still have some of the original convict-planted vines. No one had the heart to uproot them. Black Shiraz.'

As he was speaking they turned off the highway on to

a private road, gliding gently up grassy slopes and dense clumps of trees that formed a windbreak until the trees gave way to a great sea of vines with their baskets of fruit hidden under the luxuriant leaves. It was like a dream—a delicate softness in the air, a fruit and flower ambience, and somewhere borne on the breeze the tang of the orchards set to the back of the house, a much lesser interest, certainly, but a great success, especially the stone fruits.

A two-mile corridor of leafy oaks soared up ahead, sentinel lines for a semi-parkland of ornamental trees and shrubs that formed the perimeter of the historic homestead itself. The cool green cavern suddenly broke to the clear evening sky and she could see now the precise symmetry and graciousness of more formal land-scaping—broad, magnificent sweeps of lawn and terraced gardens, daffodils massing their yellow blooms under the oaks and the native gums, the beautiful evergreen mag-nolia grandiflora, towering specimens starred with giant white blooms like white tulips and here and there for variety conifers and junipers, double flowering cherry trees and the Japanese maples, wonderful lacy cover for the exquisite great drifts of indicum and kurume azaleas and rhododendrons thickly budded to the emerald green lawn. There, just as her mother had told her, were the countless camellia trees, some of them over one hundred years old, single, semi-double and doubles, from the purest white in existence, the Yukimi Guruma, through delicate pink, blush pink, silvery rose to the deep red of the Flame and the Czar.

She shook her head, and her hair fell like thick silk about her shoulders. 'I've said to myself a thousand times it couldn't come up to expectations, but now I can see for myself the long-beloved Sundown, feel its legendary

57

atmosphere.'

'Houses are houses, Gabriele. Human relationships far outweigh material possessions!'

Something in his tone stung her, but as she turned her head, he stopped the car on a grassy knoll and drew her out, his touch crackling with power, the soft touch forgotten. 'Even at this hour the house has its own magic. Look your fill of it. There, on the crest of the hill with the grape blue backdrop of the ranges.' A feeling of near anger pervaded him and the now familiar rush of aesthetic pleasure. No one, least of all this child, could be indifferent to such a high degree of perfection. Sundown, a beautiful house by anyone's standards, untampered by remodelling, a land mark in the State for all its Grecian heritage for six Doric columns soared over twenty-five feet to the hipped roof. Character and dignity and a muted classical elegance was Sundown. Strangely, like this girl herself with her delicately chiselled features, the reserved patrician look.

'It's like a crown, isn't it?' she said almost echoing his own thoughts. 'All white and golden, though the shutters are what? Shiny black?'

'Camilla's idea—a recent one. Your Aunt Camilla is, in her way, a brilliant woman. With the aid of Sir Joshua's money, she has built up a rare and beautiful collection of antiques.'

'Almost everyone loves beautiful things!' she said rather crisply for her, remembering her own dear mother's flawless taste—not that they could afford more than the odd fine object.

'Fantastic as it may seem to you, Gabriele, that's not quite true. Quite a few of Camilla's friends, wealthy even by Sir Joshua's standards, have homes that seem to me excessively vulgar. Camilla has quality.'

'You admire her?'

'I do!'

'And you're something of a snob?'

'Ah, the liberated woman! Yes, little one, in some ways I suppose I am. You must forgive me. I must blame it on the way I was brought up. My mother had unerring taste—for fashion, for flowers, for furnishings, for decoration of all kind. She would have admired you, Gabriele, she loved the beauty of restraint. Glitter meant nothing to my mother, only lustre!' She saw the tightness of his jaw and the hardness around his eyes and mouth, and all sorts of little fears struck her as though she had come on a secret place.

'I'm sorry! I'm sorry!' she said as though she was trying to reason with him, and shivered a little as though all the old emotional entanglements were her own, her own serenity gone for ever, taken over by a peculiar form of excitement. Somehow this unknown, strange man had got under her skin, and her pale young face looked suddenly taut with fatigue.

'You're sorry. You're sorry! What for, you foolish child?' Engrossed as he was in his own rather bitter reflections, he still felt the tremor that ran through her, a leaf before the wind, betraying his own resolution not to touch her. Her innocence, her tender sensitivity and her age were all too apparent, a barrier far more than an invitation to a man of his kind. He had never anticipated that she would have such power to move him, the old fierce protective feelings, and all so simply achieved.

With a deliberate, rhythmic movement, his arm dropped to encircle just as she turned her face into his shoulder. It was entirely spontaneous on both sides, a fluid, never foreign impulse.

'Cry if you want to,' he said in a hard, impassive voice.

'Don't think of me. I'm not important!'

Had she wanted to escape she couldn't have, but she did not want to escape. One could draw strength from such strength and he would never notice it. All the happy events of her life seemed to marshal themselves before her. Her mother's sweet voice saying over and over ... 'You'll love it, my darling! Sundown. Sweet Sundown!' She was seized with grief. Tears stung her eyes, but she would not give way to them. It would make everything so much worse.

'Would it matter, do you think, to spoil this beautiful jacket?' The words hurt her throat as she tried to swallow back the tears and he smiled.

'Not in the least. I was just wondering what I'd do with you!'

Gabriele lifted her head quickly with an odd, whirling sensation, conscious of a peace in her heart but a quickening in her veins. As though he was perfectly aware of her difficulties his hand dropped to her shoulder to turn her back towards the car. 'I think I must have known you, Gabriele, many, many years ago—perhaps in a kingdom by the sea. You have that look about you. Whatever it is, for all the differences between us, we seem to speak the same language. If you have any problems, come to me!'

It was an order, plainly, and she pushed back her heavy silky hair with a gesture of obedience and comfort. 'Yes!' she said automatically, and glancing down at her pale head near his shoulder he saw that she had lost just a little of that lost and alone vulnerability, but his own misgivings about this visit to Sundown, far from abating, had sharply increased. Far better for Gabriele had she been a gauche and malleable schoolgirl. Camilla would have taken a casual, faintly contemptuous pride in beating that problem. Camilla could put even the plainest girl together, all she needed was a grain of potential. It gave her, he knew, a continuing sense of creativity, a consolidation of power. It was almost certain that this child had no clear conception of her own enormous potential. In the colourful, scented blaze of Camilla's melange she would be as soft and ravishing as the dawn. How would it affect all of them? Camilla was the mistress of Sundown, brilliant and shamelessly sexy, physically and psychological provoking excitement. There was the slight chance that she might underestimate the lofty purity of innocence. Whatever other qualitites she possessed, generosity towards her own kind, her own kin, wasn't one of them.

Beside him, unaware of his ironic speculations, Gabriele walked across the soft springy grass in a mood of soft reverie and melancholy. Her Aunt Camilla had always been such a fascinating mystery, but she would love her as surely as she had loved her own dear mother, as surely as she loved the tranquil beauty of the flourishing foothills and Sundown, standing alone in its original purity, looking towards the large ornamental lake stroked by the evening breezes still guarded by a classical nymph who trailed one white hand towards the lotus blooms that grew near the reeds of her feet.

Gabriele caught her breath as she always did when she saw something beautiful. She looked up at the man with a slight curve to her lovely mouth but found his eyes remote, as the sea is remote even with the sun on it. This was his distant mood and she was to see it often, but now, for a very different reason than she imagined. She thought he wasn't going to say anything else, but she was mistaken. He took her hand and turned her to face him with the silvery lancing look she had first received from him.

'Welcome to Sundown, little one!' he said, and something in his expression told her she had found a powerful protector if not a friend. A man like Kyle Tyson whose life and living was made up of big business and intrigue and counter-intrigue, a maelstrom of success and all that went with it, would only seek the company of a woman of his own level—beauty and breeding and every social accomplishment. The end product. A woman like Aunt Camilla or one of her charmed circle. Certainly not Gabriele Somerville, student, of hardly more consequence than the swarms of itinerant pickers, some on working holidays, who would swarm over the estate towards the end of the summer. A lot was to happen to her before then. Fragile she might be, like the reeds that grew round the lake, but she had learnt, like them, to bend with the wind.

CHAPTER FOUR

THE voice floated down the stairway, seductive even in the heat of anger and frustration, and they could only stand there listening under an exquisite chandelier that dripped crystal.

'I tell you, Paul, I'm tired, sick to death of your stupid, incessant jealousy! After fourteen years one might have thought you'd passed a pinnacle or had your due quota, but instead it's like being surrounded by a million avid eyes. You grow worse, if that's possible. Won't you ever tire of the same blasted theme?'

In the marble-floored entrance hall, a Chinese Chippendale mirror with its elaborate gilt frame threw back their reflections—Gabriele, pale, wraithlike, with her silver-gilt hair streaming to her shoulders, shock and dismay in the shadowed hollows of her cheeks; Kyle Tyson, darkly, vividly handsome, his light eyes intensely alive, glittering with a kind of wry amusement. An acceptance of the human condition, the follies and illusions, the cloud castles that tumbled at a touch.

Instinctively Gabriele stepped back, in a swift kind of negation, thudding softly into Kyle Tyson's hard shoulder. His hand fell to her shoulder and she twisted her head to look up at him, seeking counsel.

'*Amor vincit omnia*, or so they'd have us believe!' he said dryly.

Above them the husky voice came to life again, moving back into earshot. 'You're half tight, anyway!' it said with withering finality, pushing home the last rivet.

'And why not?' The answering voice was querulous, sarcastic, strangely lacking in vigour. 'Not bad when you consider the quantity that's gone down my throat—Homeric for these days. Besides, what else is there for me to do? You're the one who has all the fun and the games.'

'Games, you fool!' the husky voice slashed at him, so that even Gabriele winced in shocked fascination. 'I'm not playing this time and I'm not staying in either. *I'm not!*'

'You could have a shot at it, but you don't give a damn, do you?' It sounded more despairing than accusing the way he said it. 'I know you have no loyalty, precious little moral sense ...!'

'Oh, shut up! You're impossibly banal, and for *you*, grotesque! Stay in, he says! What, and flutter about you? What a thrill! You know as well as I do, I outgrew you years ago.'

'And I damned well know why! It's ...'

A door slammed crisply and seemly, closing the dialogue.

'Lost to us!' Kyle Tyson remarked into the ringing void. 'Just as I was hanging on every word. Camilla would be perfect for Edwardian drama—a great lady, thwarted passions, a great house. I must suggest it to her.'

'So what happens now?' Gabriele asked rather defiantly.

'I'm almost tempted to have a drink myself!' His mouth, shapely and mobile, broke into a smile. 'So you still believe in fairy tales, Gabriele?'

'At the moment, my disenchantment is fairly complete. I feel terribly furtive!'

'Oh, don't be absurd!' he chopped her off neatly.

Worldly, impervious, the light note in his voice dancing over tension. 'Perhaps the whole thing's a gag!'

'I don't think so!'

'No, I can see that. Goggle-eyed as a small child! Why not think of it as symbolic of marriage, these little spats. Slanging matches if you like. Do you wonder I remain a happy bachelor?'

In the mirror their eyes met, his so full of light and diablerie that Gabriele gave a little gurgle in her throat, as fresh and charming as a child. His eyes looked beyond her to the airy opulence of the chandelier. 'I suppose every prism could tell a story. Shall we go out and come in again? After all, the front door was wide open!'

'Why not call straight out, we've arrived?'

A corner of his mouth lifted attractively. 'For all your angelic appearance, you have an authentic streak of mischief. Officially, I suppose, we're loitering, otherwise I'd think we were deliberately being kept waiting.'

'Then there's no harm in giving that dong thing a try, surely?'

'That *dong thing*, my child,' he reproved her, 'came out of a shrine. The Wheel of the Law. Repoussée silver. Pre-eighteenth century.'

'I daren't hit it, in that case.' Her eye travelled rather soberly around the handsome proportions of the main hall, the lovely ceiling of flat leaf patterns, the white and gold of the elaborate mouldings, contrasting with the polished woodwork of the doors and staircase, the elegant assemblage of furnishings and antiques, the paintings that ascended the stairs. 'I'll be lost here!'

'I don't think so!' His voice turned vaguely satirical. 'You have decided style of your own.'

'You can't be serious?'

'I am!' There was something astringent in the light,

bracing tone. 'We all have a place in the scheme of things, Gabriele. You belong here.'

She shook her head in something like denial, her hair falling over her shoulder in a silvery slide. He was looking at her in that straight, searching way of his, but to have returned his gaze was beyond her, like an inbuilt command from the brain. Signals like that could not be ignored no more than if the marble floor beneath her feet was vibrating. When she finally did look up, he had moved a few feet away from her, completely self-possessed, his hard, masculine mouth curving in the beginnings of a smile.

'It was very fortunate for me you were coming this way!' she said out of sheer nervous reaction.

'Very fortunate!' he agreed, in a grave, mocking tone, so that she coloured, the blood racing up under her matt, white skin. He was standing directly under the brilliant wash of light from the chandelier, but instead of robbing him of colour, the whole impression was one of striking vitality, a physical elegance that hit at her forcibly as if she had never until this moment laid eyes on him. It was like coming out of a tunnel into broad daylight, only the light was too dazzling and she couldn't see her way.

'You're giving me such an odd, distracted look, Gabriele,' he complained.

'Am I? I'm sorry. It's all that fabulous light!' she lied.

He lifted his dark head in his faintly arrogant fashion. 'You'll find a splendid assortment of beautiful things to look at and admire in this house. Your Aunt Camilla has impeccable judgment. In fact, in the business, her eye is legend.'

'I can believe that!' Gabriele murmured sincerely, her own eye on a pair of exquisite cloisonné vases of that lovely turquoise that characterised so much of the

Chinese work. 'But how do we resolve our own particular crisis? Father used to say, when you put your money on a horse, let it run, and I put my money on that gong!'

'I like the sound of your father!' Kyle Tyson laughed gently, and stopped. 'As it happens, little one, there *is* a way out of our predicament, but I was enjoying our little vigil. However...' He took her arm and drew her carefully out of the front door, at the same time lifting his dark resonant voice so that it carried to the furthest point of the hall and in a manner of speaking to the gods.

'Your Aunt Camilla, you'll find,' he said informatively, 'is very active in community affairs, one of our leading hostesses, and Sundown has always lent itself to extensive entertaining. All the year round. The house really comes to life when Camilla gives one of her famous parties!' He glanced briefly at Gabriele's pale head, her faint look of flurry, and laughed in his throat, the merest sound. 'That should get some response. At least I'm able to do that!' He brought down his gaze on Gabriele's face, idle, soft, and definitely amused, his eyes with that particular sheen of silver. 'Now, what's up? I thought I was perfect!'

The moment could not be averted. A shiver started at her white nape and ran down her spine as though she was witness to some piece of magic. He caught the point of her chin in his hand and made her look at him, her grave eyes long-lashed and iridescent, touchingly defenceless.

'Gabriele, Gabriele,' he said softly.

Above them a door thudded. There was a tantalising flurry along the gallery, then a soft lilting voice with a faint husky undertone—a truly feline voice, thrilling, but Gabriele didn't recognise it then. All she knew was it

67

sounded like Mamma, but Mamma playing a role foreign to her nature. The tears sprang to her eyes.

'Heavens, Kyle, it can't be you!' the voice said vitally. 'But, darling, couldn't you have rung me? Let me know you'd be early. And Gabby, my own sister's child!'

'Camilla, how charming!' Kyle threw up his dark head. His light, ironic tone betrayed nothing, but just for a moment Gabriele glimpsed another man, not nearly so kind. Arrogance and authority was all over her, an all-conquering, well-practised charm.

It was like a study in slow motion for Gabriele to replay over and over in the long months ahead. There was an indefinable change in his expression, something instant and magnetic that sprang between him and the woman on the stairs, palpable enough to make Gabriele swallow dryly. Human emotions were too tangled, too complex for her to unweave. She was far too inexperienced, a prey, herself, to inexplicable, shifting emotions. Here at long last was her Aunt Camilla, and no one and nothing had really prepared her, not even the physical imprint of her mother so clearly stamped there.

Camilla Lynnton was luscious, like a velvety rose, dark crimson, clinging effortlessly to its ultimate, full bloom, perfection, heady with fragrance. She took the breath away, an established, highly cultivated beauty in a magnificent background; her gown, the flush and glow of her flawless skin, the perfection of her *maquillage*, *the* enormous doe eyes, glowing with ten thousand secrets. She was the embodiment of woman, incredibly sexy, vibrating with exquisite passions denied everyone.

Gabriele simply could not absorb the sight of her all at once, though Kyle Tyson appeared to be having no difficulty at all; his shimmery eyes were full of male speculation. 'Blood is thicker than water after all!' he said dryly. 'Especially in adversity!' There was a superb insolence in the tilt of his head. 'Come on down, Camilla, you look gorgeous, we're all in agreement.'

Even a woman as schooled and sophisticated as her Aunt Camilla could betray herself. The creamy skin flushed with colour, the little throaty laugh was laced with excitement. 'I've said it before, Kyle, and I'll say it again, you could get away with murder. I know, darling, I know!' Her dark eyes flew on to Gabriele and Gabriele could have cried aloud at the pain of it all. Identical in shape and setting, but never the expression!

'Gabby!' the sweet, husky voice made the ugly nickname a sound of pure delight. She was gliding towards Gabriele swiftly, smiling as she came, her ravishing black georgette dinner dress glittering with intricate bands of silver and gold bugle beads, her velvety gaze compelling. 'I hope Kyle has been looking after you? Welcome to Sundown, my dear child. But you're not a child, are you? You're a young woman and a pretty one too, when I get you some decent clothes!'

Never in her life before had Gabriele felt truly awkward, but she did now. Aunt Camilla, like her mother, was petite, so that Gabriele had to incline her head faintly to receive that warm, perfumed kiss. The wonderful, heavily lashed eyes travelled over her, from her bare shining head, down the long, slender bones and exquisite young legs to the inexpensive, champagne-coloured sandals that went with her outfit. Aunt Camilla would never have said it, but Gabriele had the decided impression that she looked a mess, or at best, insignificant.

'How marvellous to have you here, dearest, and you're going to be such a help to me!' she *did* say, very graciously, a smile quirking the full, luscious mouth.

'In what way?' Kyle asked in his unquenchable

fashion, and Camilla swirled round to him as fragrant and fragile as a hothouse flower.

'Now, now, Kyle, *I'm* not part of the Organisation!'

'What a pity, when I'm sure it would benefit us all,' he returned silkily, and Camilla gave a trill of laughter, like a blackbird's in the sudden, fraught silence. 'You could teach me how. *You*, who can manage us all!'

'With more to forfeit than to be gained,' he said with bitter smoothness, his silvery gaze cool and deliberate until Camilla tossed it aside with a movement of her rippling dark head, almost a true jet.

'You're an unspeakable joy, Kyle, whatever else you are, but please yourself. The Crawfords' tonight—you're going?'

'Regrettably, no. I've just told Denise Danton the same thing!'

'Ah, Denise! Such surplus energy and for a woman her age!' The huge, velvety eyes sparkled with pleasure and challenge. 'I can see my role is to wait. Is it?'

'You did warn me!' He declined to pick up the challenge. His gaze ranged over Camilla's shoulder to Gabriele, standing cool and fair, remote as a swan, gliding over all the swirling undercurrents, seemingly safe from them.

'I'm long since due back in town. I'll take my leave of you, Gabriele. Whenever you decide, I'd like to take you to dinner, show you around some of our better vineyards. You can reach me at the office. Camilla has the number.'

Gabriele stepped forward with her quiet manner, holding out her hand. 'That's very kind of you, Mr. Tyson. I'd like that!' she said gently, with a surfacing instinct for self-preservation. It was perfectly plain that here she would have to tread warily, as if under the marble was

70

a minefield.

She might not have understood him very well, but he seemed to see through her with exceptional clarity. The very triteness made him smile and in that smile was a brilliant, fleeting dash of mischief and pure friendliness. Perhaps the friendliness was apparent, for Camilla's white, jewelled hand seemed to relax.

'You can't imagine how many women you'll have jealous of that. You're honoured, Gabby, my pet!' The sweet voice lapped the air like a lute. She came to stand beside Gabriele, slipping an arm around her narrow waist. She looked superbly confident, secure in her own wealth and beauty like a great actress, for whom it would be an incredible piece of foolishness or an exercise in futility for any woman to try to upstage her. Her own sister, almost her double, had not been able to do that.

For an interminable moment Kyle didn't move, his eyes like crystal on the picture they made—as spectacular in its way as Camilla could have wished. The blazing power of one, the pale tranquillity of the other. They were a striking pair, Odette and Odile. He glanced smoothly away, his face giving away nothing, black-haired and sardonic, while Camilla broke the tableau to slide one bare white arm along the dark cloth of his sleeve.

'I'll come down to the car with you, Kyle. I owe you a little something!'

Fairly commonplace words, Gabriele thought, to have achieved what they did. A tightening of his facial muscles, a line between the narrowed eyes that sparkled like sequins. She found she couldn't watch.

'I won't be a moment, Gabby!' Camilla called over her shoulder. 'Go up if you like, dearest. Your room is the fourth on the right from the top of the stairs. Paula's old room. She used to love it.'

All else was obliterated by the mention of her mother's name. He could see that. Without another word or a glance, Gabriele turned and began to walk up the beautiful curving staircase almost like a sleepwalker, except for the tightened white hand that gripped the gleaming cedar. She was almost on line with the chandelier that turned slightly in the evening breeze showering its radiance all over her, tinkling like the laughter that later drifted in from the wide verandah. What one wished for too deeply never did come true!

In the end, it was the children who showed Gabriele to her room, emerging from the far end of the corridor, scampering like the puppy at their feet in their haste and eagerness to meet their new cousin.

'Oh, golly, Gabriele! You *do* look an angel. The Blessed Damozel or someone. I love your hair. I'm Melissa. That's Mozart, our Peke, Beethoven's locked up . . . and Paul, of course!' This as an afterthought. 'We're cousins, aren't we? Isn't that funny? We don't look a bit alike. We are sorry about your mother and father. Uncle Kyle told us. He said we would have to love one another that bit harder!'

'I should say you'd be very easy to love!' Gabriele interrupted the torrential recital. 'How are you, Melissa . . . Paul? It's lovely to meet you at long last. My own little cousins!' She held out both hands, and the children, boy and girl, both tawny gold like Mozart, Melissa with wide, familiar dark eyes, took a firm grip on each one, pulling her along the extra few feet to her room, with Mozart nipping ecstatically at her heels, ruining one stocking.

'Mamma had it done specially!' Melissa announced,

pushing open the door with a surprisingly tattered slippered foot. ''Course, it's nothing like Mamma's!'

'Nothing is!' Paul supplied, speaking for the first time, although he had been constantly smiling. Melissa was the one who would provide the ever-constant source of information.

'It's beautiful!' Gabriele murmured, dispelling two slightly anxious expressions. Privately she might have wished it had been left in all its old nostalgic charm. This wasn't the room her mother had described, except for the bed. There couldn't be two the same.

'It should be!' Melissa was grousing like an old woman under pressure than ever before. 'It cost a sinful lot of money.'

'Sinful!' Paul snorted, picking up Mozart who was wrinkling up his forehead. 'Whose word was that? Lissa's always listening at keyholes, so don't trip over her. Anyway, the bed's the same!'

'It's brilliant! A fourposter!' Melissa ignored him. 'I wish I had one.'

'Not with *your* dreams!'

Melissa turned her back on him, to beam on her cousin. 'I have terrific dreams. Shall I tell you about them?'

'Better not, she'll collapse!' Paul said, full of prior knowledge.

'I'd like to hear as soon as I'm settled in,' Gabriele said kindly. 'Now, where do those French doors lead?'

'To the outside balcony,' Melissa said, following the red herring, and Paul winked. 'My bedroom's a mess,' she sighed, 'and *his* is a den. Mamma won't listen to any suggestions. Children must be housed as cheaply as possible. Do you like your colour scheme? White, yellow and lemon. It's sunny, isn't it?'

'Yes. Serene yet sophisticated. Aunt Camilla is very clever.'

'She's that!' Paul supplied very oddly indeed.

'The bedspread is lovely,' Gabriele continued, her thoughtful eyes on his face. 'Crisp white eyelet and fluffy pillows balance that fabulous bed. I've never slept in a fourposter before.' She wandered around the large, high-ceilinged room with three pairs of eyes on her. 'A chaise-longue covered in silk damask. Two Empire chairs with beautiful crewel embroidery and a long low table in front of the mantel. We'll be able to have lots of chats there. A Directoire desk and an elegant chair and for a touch of extravagance a collection of miniature paint-ings—eighteenth-century by the look of them!' Gently she touched an enamelled ivory oval. 'A lady by Andrew Plimmer. How lovely!'

'You're pretty clever yourself!' Melissa said admir-ingly. 'What's the desk? A Director? My father's a director. Sir Joshua's the Chairman of the Board, but Uncle Kyle's the real boss, Dad said.'

'No, darling, the desk is *Directoire*—a style of period furnishing, French. I'll explain it to you some time. My father was an architect. I've always been interested in such things, but we didn't have the beautiful things you've got.'

'They belong to Sir Joshua,' Paul explained briefly, sounding odd again. 'Mamma can buy what she likes, but it really belongs to Sir Joshua. I don't like him much. Some days he's all right, but . . .'

'What's wrong with *him*?' Melissa asked, referring to Mozart who had set up a howl.

'Perhaps he feels unwanted,' Gabriele suggested, glad to get off the subject of Sir Joshua. Even children had problems. 'Why don't you pick him up again?'

74

'He's neurotic, that's what!' Paul pronounced, doing just that. 'You'll find out when you get to know him. Some days all you *can* do is let him watch the television. He loves that!'

'And what about Beethoven? I suppose he likes to play the piano?'

'No, actually, he's a she, and she's having puppies,' Melissa said.

'Well, no one claims it's an easy existence!' Gabriele smiled. 'Any cats?'

'Only one, Lucrezia. She doesn't pay the least attention to any of us, yet we all respect her.'

'Cats are aristocratic!' Gabriele pronounced, giving Melissa's chin a light tap. 'I suppose they think it beneath them. You should never give them too much leeway all the same, otherwise they oppose all commands on principle.'

'I'm so glad you've come,' said Melissa, in total collapse on the chair. 'It's been hell around here lately!'

'Oh dear!' Gabriele looked up in dismay at the bearded giant who materialised in her doorway. Henry the Eighth in his younger days, she thought fancifully, all tawny gold and vivid blue eyes, a strikingly handsome man even if he was a few stone overweight.

'Don't take any notice of me,' he said in the voice she recalled. 'As far as the kids are concerned I'm just another kid. Not a very smart one at that!'

'Oh, Dad!' Paul said unhappily, 'have you ever thought you're just plain lazy?'

'No, son, it's not that. Basically I'm a shy, insecure sort of person. One of the outstanding neurotic personalities of our time!'

'I thought *Mozart* was that!' said Paul, chewing his lip.

'I'm glad to see my son doesn't substitute psychology

75

for plain common sense. I hope to God's he's always like that!' Paul Lynnton senior remarked with a sideways glance at Gabriele. 'For reasons that are probably clear to her alone, my wife has written me off. The kids have learnt early in life to adapt. Just as well, their mother is quite ignorant of their emotional needs. Don't look so sad, Paula's girl. You've only arrived and right away conflict sets in. You're very good-looking, but even without your looks you'll have an assured entrée to all the best places. Camilla will see to that.'

'I've come to meet you and the children, Uncle Paul,' Gabriele said quietly. 'See the house where my dear, dear mother was born. Sleep in her bed.'

The utter sincerity and seriousness of her tone got through to him, for his high colour deepened. 'You're very welcome, my dear, on one hundred counts. I only had the pleasure of meeting your mother and father once, at my own wedding. I regret many things, too late! God, I need a drink!'

'Oh, Dad!'

'I need a drink, son, when I'm browned off, which is all the time.' The heavy shoulders slouched a bit. 'Besides, I've had extreme demands made on me today. Most big men, and I'm well over six feet, have at least an illusion of superiority, but I've never had that. What's wrong with me?'

'Perhaps you need something to eat?' Gabriele suggested, a jewel of diplomacy. 'I'm starving myself!' This, at a time when her appetite had deserted her.

'Now that strikes me as a brilliant idea!' Paul cried, pleasure flooding his pale golden skin. 'People who can't eat are horribly frustrated. Mamma's going out in lashings of beads and georgette, and we'll have a party. You can have a drink if you like, Dad.'

76

'A party, I'd like that.' Melissa exploded to her feet, buckling her father's knees. 'Why not?'

'Why not indeed?' He lifted her high above his head, lowered her, kissed her gleefully, then set her on her feet. 'Come and give me a kiss as well, Gabriele. I'm old enough to be your father, so I suppose it's all right.'

There was something very lost and likeable about him. She could see that. The children, who resembled him greatly, loved and grieved for him, for whatever reason. It was written all over their happy/unhappy little faces. What use was money and a beautiful home if it bred problems like these? Nothing was ever as it seemed. Obviously Mozart with his super-intelligence was on her own wave length, for he took the opportunity of letting out an ear-piercing whine which caused young Paul to swoop on him and haul him off with a look of all owners of importunate pups.

'Come on, Lissa, let's put him out on the grass. See you at dinner, everyone!'

'Something festive,' his father ordered from the French doors, without viewing their progress. 'Tell Marie, she'll attend to it.'

'Uncle Paul?' There was something in his stillness alone that she didn't like. 'Come here, Gabby girl, something I think you'd prefer to know. All I might wish to be. All I never *can* be!' She came to stand by his side, following his sombre gaze to the courtyard below. 'The glorious Camilla her admirer, drawing seekers to her side. Kyle's proving more difficult than all the rest put together, but it only adds spice. Camilla commands allegiance, or else!'

'Might you be mistaken?' she asked, an odd taste of wretchedness in her own mouth.

'The rift between my wife and me is perfectly patent.

77

It would be very hard to say if Kyle is interested or not. At any rate he hasn't enlightened *me*. To a certain extent even Kyle toes the line so far as my grandfather is concerned, scandal is unthinkable.'

'Yet he had one of his own!' She could have bitten her tongue out the moment she had said it, but she was provoked herself.

Unexpectedly Paul laughed. 'My dear girl, the Old Man is a law unto himself. Certainly he idolised Kyle's mother, a woman many, many years his junior, but as to the rest, *I* don't know and I'm damned sure Kyle doesn't either, and the Old Man's not saying even if he knows himself. You women! Any rate it's an enormous whodunnit. The odd part is, I admire Kyle enormously. He's tough and he's not above a bit of non-stop intrigue, but he plays fair—in business anyway. I'll tell you, and it's a secret between us, I'm worried. What Camilla wants, she gets, and she wants Kyle Tyson. You can tell that at a glance. If she kisses him I'll swear I'll pitch that jar thing!'

'Not necessary,' Gabriele breathed. 'Mr. Tyson didn't strike me as at all decadent!'

'He's the devil himself beside me!'

'He's getting into the car anyway. You can open your eyes.'

'Ablaze with relief,' he said mildly. 'Come, child, I feel like a sneak-thief!' His tawny brows lifted, a rare self-disgust in his voice. 'I *am* sorry, Gabriele, unburdening my problems. It's not right at all! Besides, this only creates new tensions and perhaps all for nothing. We'll find out in time.' His voice was slurring a little and Gabriele heard it. There was a small silence and he shook his head, whether or not to clear it she couldn't tell. His expression was rueful, not like another, dark and de-

78

tached. She heard herself saying calmly, her silver hair glittering, 'Do you think I could have my luggage up, please, Uncle Paul? It's on the veranda. I think I'll change for the party.'

His smile flickered and he swung around with good grace. 'Why, of course, my dear. I'll see it's done right away. You don't have anything green, do you? That's my favourite colour. Now, there are things to be done and I'm on my way. I'm glad you're here, Gabriele. You're a nice girl. You'll be good for all of us.'

She smiled at him serenely, inwardly deeply disturbed. What a mess for a new guest with her own stomach doing somersaults, and with reason perhaps. First impressions were accurate enough.

CHAPTER FIVE

BEFORE a week had gone past, Gabriele realised that whatever dream picture she had drawn of her Aunt Camilla, it bore little resemblance to the real woman. Camilla Lynnton was no replica of her sister and countless thousands of other women, absorbed in their husbands and children, the hundred and one interests that centred about the home, her main preoccupation was herself, as though so perfect a flower could afford little time for anything else than maintaining its own perfection. At an age when most women were showing a few wrinkles, the skin of her face and throat, her slender seductive body held the bloom and elasticity of youth. Her attention to detail was enormous, greatly enhancing these natural assets. The creams and lotions, the most expensive on the market, packaging was important; the same product in a plain tube would never have done; her make-up, applied with an artist's hand; her lustrous hair which required professional attention several times a week and sometimes twice in the same day depending on the function; her exquisite clothes; her diet régime which wasn't as strenuous as one might have thought for so rewarding a result.

She was sweetness itself to the children. She never raised her voice, never scolded, but they couldn't lay claim to holding her attention, for she was always on the way in or out. Besides, what else were the household staff for, and now Gabriele, a godsend. She said so herself. What little time there was left over from self was commendably given over to the big social and civic functions for this and that charity campaign and plenty of Press cuttings for the scrapbook Melissa was keeping up as a substitute figure. To Gabriele, already entrenched in her cousin's affections, she was equally sweet if not sweeter, so that Gabriele, in the nicest, most insidious way possible, found herself run off her feet answering the telephone and sending off batches of thank-you cards, and supervising the children, which really was no chore at all. and they all seemed to enjoy the hunt for the car keys that went on several times a day and resulted in the fact that Camilla invariably had them herself—'In my handbag, would you believe?'

For her husband, she reserved a smiling, civilised contempt only lightly glossed over by an impeccable public manner. What went on in private Gabriele could only guess at with that very first evening as a reference. However, a constant stream of friends and acquaintances seemed to drift in, when husband and wife went through the conventional motions of a loving, lovable couple, with Camilla the pick of the two, coveted by most of the men so that it seemed to Gabriele the whole thing was a gigantic con trick. Coming as she had done from a hard-to-come-by happy home she took it hard when almost anyone, the children even, could have told her this state of affairs was far from uncommon. Nothing in the way her mother and father had behaved prepared her the climate at Sundown.

There were many things she would have to learn, and learn them soon. Already at eight her little friend and cousin Melissa had a sharper appreciation of the status quo, not to speak of a degree of cynicism. It was sad and regrettable, but it was true. Lying awake at night remembering her mother's wonderful qualities, her essential *niceness* was enough to make her ebb into tears. What her mother had thought of as virtues, Aunt Camilla would probably write off as vices. What her mother had taught her was totally unimportant, seemed to obsess Aunt Camilla; the right people, the right clothes, the right places, all with a vast and charming intolerance for what concerned the masses. Thousands of people could be starving or dying and Aunt Camilla would say: 'How terrible!' because it *was* terrible, but what really caused her anguish was the imaginary blemish she sought in any one of the gilded and scrolled antique mirrors that gave back her vivid reflection.

Yet it was impossible to deny the force of her attraction like a painting that fascinated as much as it appalled. It went so far in heightening the senses, then left one empty, grasping for its true essence. Gabriele, who wished only to love her, was made to accept, like Paul and Melissa, that Camilla had her own standards and if privately Gabriele thought them rotten then a lot of people lived by them, many of the women for whom Aunt Camilla played hostess. Indeed, it seemed to Gabriele's intent eye, they were almost identical in voice and manner, their style of dressing, their attitudes and interests, their assured self-indulgence.

'Spoiled, silly bitches! They ought to be taken in hand!' Sir Joshua was fond of exclaiming well within earshot, or so young Paul informed her with fatalistic calm. Gabriele had not attempted to reprove him. She couldn't, not when she was so much in agreement. For the first time she thought of Sir Joshua Lynnton as a real person.

With Sir Joshua in mind, Camilla came round to the business of outfitting Gabriele according to her 'standards'. There were many, many, people Gabriele would soon meet who would remember her mother as one of the Beautiful Lawrence Girls. It was unthinkable that

Gabriele should let the image down, especially when Sir Joshua didn't seem to care two hoots what Camilla spent as long as he got results. The 'child', meaning Gabriele, was to be provided with a suitable wardrobe and whatever else she might wear. It would seem a good idea, also, to have the 'child' enroll at the University at her earliest oportunity. Naturally she would finish her course there. Alone in the world, virtually an orphan, Gabriele, unknown to her, was about to be taken over like a business venture, but with more heart to it than she might have supposed. However inaccessible he might have become, Sir Joshua still lent his ear to at least one, and that one had come out strongly for the new arrival.

Gabriele, however, being young and sensitive to the point of being touchy, reacted oddly to the news of the proposed shopping tour.

'I've quite enough to see me through the rest of my visit, Aunt Camilla.' She hadn't the least intention of being taken over and wished to get that straight. Not for nothing was the soft cleft in her chin. She stood in the middle of that breathtaking bed-sitting room that faced the flower-laden courtyard, fit for the Empress of Iran, her normally smoky grey eyes almost stormy.

Far from being impressed, Camilla was inclined to be amused. The young were so boring, especially ones who took themselves as seriously as this niece of hers. 'But, dearest, Sir Joshua expects it!' she said mildly, swinging her slender white arms over her head, propped up in her beautiful bed.

All the languor and boneless grace of Lucrezia, the pedigree Persian, Gabriele thought wryly. The enormous doe eyes were wide and alert, not a fatigue line marred the creamy-skinned face, the small, high breasts revealed by the chiffon lace nightgown were those of a young girl. Wonderful, Gabriele thought, one had to admire her. Not even Mamma could have rivalled such splendour—but then Mamma never tried.

'What are you thinking?' Camilla enquired, stretching luxuriously.

'How beautiful you are!'

'What a dear. You really are the dearest child! So listen to me. I know how you feel, but there you are! There are times one must sink one's independence. For my sake. Besides, dearest, you're not a woman at all if you don't like new clothes. I couldn't possibly let you appear at one of my parties in what you've brought here. Paula really should have stepped in there. Why, she was a beautiful dresser before she was married, whatever else she might have become. You simply can't let me down. I won't hear of it. Why, people would say ... However could Camilla Lynnton have such a dowdy niece? In any case, some very dear friends of mine are returning from Europe at the end of the week. I'm giving a little party for them on Saturday night, about sixty or seventy. I don't want you creeping about like a white mouse. You're a quiet girl, aren't you? Paula was so vivacious—not that I don't love you as my very own. I promise you, dearest, you won't know yourself by the time I'm finished with you. It's rather exciting really. You have the potential if you'd only let yourself go. Too stiff and reserved!'

'I'd much rather not, Aunt Camilla!'

Apparently opposition was incredible, for Camilla frowned, a thing she took care not to do. 'If it's the money that's bothering you, dear, Sir Joshua has more than enough in the purse. Why, the wicked old dear hasn't put a foot wrong in the past fifty years!'

'I've no wish to distress you ...'

84

'Then why *do* you?' Sweetly she relented. 'Foolish child to think I'd let you. Come, Gabby, don't act the silly prude. Such a bore. A woman can get anything in this world if she knows how. All the people we know will be there. I see nothing disgraceful or degenerate in out-fitting you properly, can you?'

'Put like that, Aunt Camilla, *no*, but I'm sure . . .'

'Whatever are you quibbling about, Gabby?' Camilla said, faintly caustic. 'You've too much delicacy in these matters. Like your father, not that it did him much good, so be warned. Now, let's settle this once and for all or I shall go black in the face with rage, and no one would like that at all. You've been such a help to me, dearest, don't spoil everything now. The children love you. They've been quite voluble on that score. By the way,' this very off-hand, 'have you contacted Kyle Tyson at all?'

'Not as yet!' Gabriele came up with the right answer. 'I feel he was only being kind, and I don't like to impose on such a busy man.'

'I know you don't, and I admire you for it!' Camilla said in her soft lilt. 'Actually, Gabby, it might be a good idea if you don't contact him at all. Kyle *is* Kyle, if you know what I mean. Young and inexperienced as you are, you still must have felt his enormous sex appeal. Older and wiser women than you have come a cropper. Best leave well alone. Really, it's not suitable. I'll arrange something to save all our faces. Leave it to me. Now, could you run my bath for me, dearest. Thank you, you're an angel. I'll be ready about twoish, if that suits you. What a pity we're not of a size, I could have lent you something to wear into town, but never mind. I know the most marvellous place. We should be able to get most things there. It will save time too. I'm going out tonight. In fact, I think I'll stay up in town—we have a penthouse apartment there. You don't mind finding your own way back. Do you drive?'

'Yes, Aunt Camilla,' Gabriele called over her shoulder, filling the pink bathroom with steam. Gold taps and rose quartz fittings, my God! A whole wall of mirrors and a chandelier. French style mouldings on the cabinets, a sunken marble tub, beautiful wallpaper with steam-resistant qualitites. Not a thing had been overlooked. She picked up a magnificent stoppered bottle in metal and glass and tipped a lavish amount of the contents into the bath.

'But, dearest,' the soft husky voice wailed from the bedroom, 'you've added the wrong bath-salts! I don't feel in the least woodsy today, but never mind.'

What Camilla had not foreseen was that, once committed, Gabriele had a decided mind of her own and what was more astounding, surprisingly good taste. Or not so surprising, as Camilla later remarked. 'After all, you *are* my niece!' The shop, as was to be expected, was the smartest and most exclusive in town and there wasn't a bit of sense walking through its elegant doors unless one was prepared to 'pay through the neck'. Camilla, or rather Sir Joshua, was. Petty in some ways, but not where quality was concerned, he had learnt the hard way that clothes were status symbols with all sections of the population and all age groups. Even the young were greatly influenced by the matchless mélange they threw together and called fashionable.

In the end, Gabriele had outfits for every occasion. 'Super!' Camilla pronounced as the dresses were twirled on their hangers in front of her. 'The way you dress affects you!' Which, to be fair, it did, so, like a mannequin, Gabriele paraded in a series of skirts and slacks and a whole collection of tops; two beautifully tailored little suits with stitch-pleated skirts and nifty jackets; a half dozen romantic long dresses for the summer evenings; a smoky grey chiffon dinner dress, one-of-a-kind, and sprinkled with something that might well have been stardust, and the pièce de résistance for Saturday night, a pure white silk jersey in the Grecian manner for a truly frightening price.

Gabriele's little mews of distress were treated with the scorn they deserved, and even Gabriele subsided as Camilla picked out for herself a ruffled, flame-coloured stunner with a matching feather boa that cost as much as all the other purchases put together. An equal distribution of privilege. After that, Gabriele opened her mouth soundlessly. Living as she had, naïvely imagining most women had to balance a budget and shop around before making the big decision Camilla's magnificent largesse reduced her to awe. Before it was all over, she had several pairs of shoes, a dozen exquisitely fine pantyhose, a 'good brand, dearest' of make-up for the dewy, pearlescent look, and plenty of cream for an already flawless skin. Her long, silver-gilt hair was shampooed and dressed into a young, stylish version of a chignon when she refused point blank to make the move to a short cut. 'Well groomed is well bred,' said Camilla, and try as she did, Gabriele could find no argument with that. Nevertheless, she was glad when it was all over; such affluence unnerved her, as though at any minute it would all prove a ghastly mistake and she would be required to foot the bill herself.

Later when she merged into the sunlight, Camilla still a willing captive of the dryer, with plans of her own, Gabriele looked a coolly beautiful young woman, elegant and independent, her beauty enhanced by one of the tailored suits with imported Italian sandals to match, both in a pale sand, matched up with a green and cream silk shirt and a single strand of big chunky beads. As a look, it was alive but ladylike, an absolute must, as Camilla had explained. One must be able to tell at a glance if one belonged to the 'right people' or not.

The sunshine was sparkling but gentle on her bare head. Like Adelaide itself, graceful like its name, a gentle, very prosperous city, tranquil like the Torrens that ran through its heart, well bred and unruffled like its traffic with none of the gay dynamism of Sydney, or the charm and self-assured stability of Melbourne, the only other two cities she knew to any degree. When she had her diploma, she would travel. Work her way around the world, but first she would see her own limitless continent from the emerald North with its inpenetrable rain forests and the incomparable Barrier Reef to the primeval fantasyland of the Dead Heart, the third largest desert in the world, that could blaze into an endless vista of wild flowers with only a shower of rain. Winter in the Alice was supposed to be superb. Or tropical Darwin. She had never seen a crocodile or a water buffalo or tens of thousands of wild geese that wheeled above the countless chains of lakes and billabongs. There was so much for her to see. She was young. There was much for her to taste and experience.

With a burst of almost forgotten enthusiasm, she crossed the road, long legs flashing, heading for one of the excellent little coffee houses that graced the city. She would have coffee and perhaps a delicious Continental concoction—chocolate, she hadn't the slightest need to watch her figure, yet—then she would sit and casually gaze at the population. She liked to study people and try to guess their backgrounds. The bistro just along to the left looked crushingly expensive, but she had to do justice to her outfit which quietly shrieked Tullo. Perhaps she was like everyone else and success would go to her head. Entertained by the idea, a charming, faintly mysterious little smile crossed her face.

'I thought it had to be you!' a voice chortled contentedly. 'To meet in the street when I've been ringing you! But, angel, how gorgeous! You, I mean. You really do look gorgeous. A swinger!'

Startled, helpless, her elbow caught in a firm grasp, Gabriele swung her head to look into Noel Danton's bright eyes, for once authentically admiring. 'Noel, how nice!' she exclaimed, in reality dismayed. 'Forgive me, I was daydreaming. How are you? Your mother?'

'Fine. Fine. A box of birds!' he dismissed Mother. 'It's you I want to talk about.' The hazel eyes were all over her. 'What have you done to yourself? Your hair! It's enough to throw me back overboard. In fact, I'm getting shivers all down my spine. How can Camilla stand it having someone so good-looking in the house? Same sex, of course, that's understood!'

'Maybe she's used to it!' Gabriele stood pliant in that possessive grasp, finding Noel and his whole style unpalatable.

'Don't look so harried, sweet!' He lowered his voice to a confidential drawl. 'I know anything I impart to you on the side will remain an absolute and irrevocable secret!'

'What proof have you got?' she challenged him.

'Your eyes. Mirrors of the soul—precisely. Such sweet, fresh innocence!'

'It sounds rather dull!'

'Not at all, not in this polished society. I say, are you coming or going? Which? I know you'll have heaps to tell me and naturally I want to know.' He shot back his cuff. 'I have to be back in the office in half an hour or so, but until then . . .' He paused significantly, as if he were locking and barring a door behind him.

'Actually, Noel——' she sought an escape route, not entering into the spirit of the thing at all, but his eyes had gone over her head, on his smooth, fair face a curiously vapid expression, half smile, half an anticipated box in the head. 'Hello there!' he called out, quite madly pleasant. Kyle Tyson, the unforeseen element to upset everything, he thought, bitterly envious. Kyle Tyson, looking as splendid as the devil himself, drat the man and his damned arrogance, the faultless way he held his head and his damned clothes that always made Noel want to change his tailor. 'Just filling in Gabriele on the local colour. Sheer coincidence we met!'

'Really? Gabriele, you don't look as if you're liking it at all. The local colour, of course.'

He was beside her and again she was caught up in his aura, the breathless involvement, the dark and sardonic voice with that edge of mockery. 'Would you mind terribly if we made off?' he asked Noel, plainly not caring at all. 'I'm taking Gabriele to one of the smart little restaurants with which this city abounds,' he explained smoothly. 'A few things to attend to first, you know how it is. Gabriele, you don't mind waiting. I'll make you as comfortable as possible.'

'No, not at all!' She was forced to meet that silvery gaze in wonder at the whole preposterous story.

'You go right ahead!' Noel said obligingly, looking keenly from one to the other, grievously affronted, but keeping a smile on his face with the greatest of efforts. Inside he was corroded with acid. Surely Gabriele was young enough to be Tyson's daughter. No, not that.

Even Kyle Tyson would have shirked fatherhood at fifteen. Yet she was reacting rather oddly in the circumstances, like a fair captive. A prize, innocent as a new drift of snow, when most of the women he knew, his dear mother included, would have given their eye teeth to have had a dinner date with Kyle Tyson, the big wheeler-dealer with more sex appeal than was actually decent.

He promised himself he would mention the whole thing to Mother. Just as she was about to have dinner. Many the scar he bore from *her*! Here now, just as he thought nothing could surprise him, was Tyson with Gabriele, like some exquisite camellia for his buttonhole. The one so dark and forceful, the other so angelically fair—and such a fast worker! It was unthinkable even if they did make a striking pair. It filled him with a wash of spite and hostility, not unpleasant really, for it carried him along on a high tide. He was jealous, but burning hot impotence made him keep face. Only for an instant did his true feelings spring out of his eyes, to be swiftly subdued. It could cost him his job.

Kyle Tyson, on the other hand, had registered all Noel's reactions with a singularly suave acceptance, too far removed to be at all affected. No, that wasn't quite true. The sight of Gabriele, silvery head bowed, in Danton's grasp had forced on him a quick decision when he seldom acted on impulse. He allowed Noel to make his goodbyes, twittering in his sophisticated fashion, in a rare burst of bravado brushing Gabriele's satiny cheek, fixing a date, 'You know!' then he made off, careful to hold himself as a man on his way back to his executive office.

'How strange to find you in such a predicament!' Tyson said dryly. 'How are you, Gabriele? I think the world would come to an end before you'd ring me of your own accord.'

'Oh, I'm sorry, you don't understand!'

'I think I do, but we're committed now. You must come with me.'

'I wish you'd tell me where!' she said with some sincerity, but he was inclined to ignore her, compelling her gently but effectively in the direction he wished to go.

'Do you want to come?' he asked her at length, his eyes flashing quicksilver.

'Yes!' Something told her to tell the truth and at once.

'Well then! I don't go along with all this Women's Liberation business. I like a woman to do what she's told. Especially when she looks as you do.'

'How?'

'Quite maddeningly elegant, as it happens. Most men are desirous of beauty, little one, and you have it in just the way I like—subtle and graceful, a reverie. I've not the least objection to dreamy women, providing they're intelligent.'

'But not intelligent enough to question your decisions?'

'Are any able to do that?' He came to a halt and she was pulled very close to him, facing him in silence, her mind fully arrested. He was looking down at her in some arrogance, head up, eyes narrowing, challenging her to make a fool of herself, like the rest of them, but she wasn't going to do that. She could, if she chose, prove a lot smarter than he gave her credit for.

'Stop smirking, Gabriele!' he said, amused and diverted. 'I'm prepared to admit there's a great deal more to you than a man might suspect!'

'That's very generous of you, Mr. Tyson. And of

course, you're right, as usual!'

'If you were a half dozen years older, I'd make you answer for that, but since there's nothing either of us can do about it . . .'

Irresistibly, Gabriele's eyes travelled over his face. 'Strange, strange are your ways, Mr. Tyson. You make me feel quite superfluous!'

'Oh, I wouldn't say that, Gabriele, it's just that I'm not used to making so little headway. Now, let's cross with the lights, shall we? And if I must repeat myself, it's Kyle!' he said silkily.

'Well then, *Kyle*,' she murmured agreeably. 'Am I to ask no questions at all?'

'For preference, no. But since you appear to be trembling slightly, it's not an abduction scene. I have one or two appointments I just cannot break. I wouldn't have dragged you in on them for the world, only you looked like you needed rescuing. A damsel in distress in the grand tradition.'

'As bad as that?'

'Yes!' he said briefly. 'I'm a good judge of faces and I was quite halted by yours. I simply had to get you out of Danton's jealous grasp.'

'Well, now you've helped me escape, am I any safer?'

'In public, yes!' He turned his dark head to look down at her and his gaze was very cool and clear under arching black brows. It was a gaze she could not sustain and despite herself she coloured and nibbled on her lower lip.

'Well, actually, Gabriele, *no*!' he said softly, his eyes brilliant on her flushed face. 'I'm the perfect image of chivalry. It's for this that I stayed.'

Faintly exasperated by his provocative mockery, the handsome rather relentless face, she surged on ahead looking neither right nor left and fell back abruptly as an aggressive and irritable young mother wielding a twin pram almost cannoned into her in a rush of resentment as much as anything else.

'See what happens when you lose your head!' Kyle said dryly, pulling her deftly away. 'Don't look so surprised.'

Her surprise, had he known it, was her reaction to the touch of his hand. A touch she had now come to recognise, as stunning in its fashion as a shining sword. She made an effort to rationalise his effect on her, to reduce the giddy state of tension, but it was impossible. Women did not rationalise in any case, though they tried hard enough to deny it. This encounter had only sharpened her desire to look at him, to hear him speak. She wondered just how much stoicism would be required to remain immune to him, but of course she wasn't immune at all. She never had been, not from the very first moment. Pure shock kept her still, but only for seconds. His downbent glance was oddly disturbing as if her every thought was right there, visible to the eye.

'What's wrong?' he asked.

'I'm not sure!'

'And I'm not sure either. Mercifully, here's the car!' His hand at her elbow, dark and compelling, he urged her towards a big, off-white Mercedes which she later came to know as the 'office car'.

'The habit of obedience dies hard. Get in, Gabriele.' He held the door for her and she slipped into the seat, grateful for the necessity of adjusting her seat belt. It gave her something to do and quietened all those funny jumpy nerves, at least until he got in. His masculinity was a live thing, profoundly stirring. There was a silence for a few moments as he waited his opportunity to join the flow of traffic, then smoothly they moved out and he put his foot down, picking up speed, calm and relaxed, his lean brown hands firm on the wheel.

'Aren't you going to ask me what I'm doing here?' she asked rather meekly.

'Quite unnecessary!'

'You *know*.' It wasn't a question at all, but a plain statement of fact.

'Perhaps I should apologise.' He flickered a shimmery glance at her, 'But I like to keep right up on things. Do you mind?'

'Right now I can only wonder where we're going!' she said defensively.

'Don't worry, you'll get a welcome,' he mocked her. 'Actually, Gabriele,' he lingered lightly over her name, 'I have an apartment at Warral Towers, not far from here. My business will take me until about six o'clock, so you can wait there for me. It will be much more comfortable Connor will take care of you. He's been with my family ever since I can remember. He makes excellent coffee. He's a great help to me with lots of things and he's the very soul of discretion.' He tilted his dark head with his customary arrogance. 'All right?'

She turned her pale head towards him, visibly collecting herself. 'There's only one thing, how shall I get back to Sundown?'

'I thought you'd never ask. I'll drive you back, of course. Getting my own way is a mania with me.'

'Oh!' she made a funny little gesture of assent. 'Quite simply done, too, I imagine. My own calmness amazes me.'

'Even I am impressed. You're what? Nineteen?'

'Twenty on Christmas Eve.'

'So? It will save another present!'

The tone of his voice, teasing and indulgent, so reminded her of her father that the tears sprang to her eyes, iridescent in her cameo face.

It was incredible the way he picked up the least little sign, his voice unexpectedly gentle when he wasn't gentle at all. 'I'm sorry, that went home, didn't it? We're never free of our remembrances.'

'I wouldn't want to be!' She touched a quick finger to her left cheekbone. 'My father used to say exactly that in that same tone of voice ... it will save another present ... Of course, I always got more than my share.'

'It would be very difficult not to love and indulge you, Gabriele, you must have been a very pretty child.'

'Do you love anyone?'

'Oh, Gabriele!'

'More classified information?' Her voice was still a little husky, recovering, and his eyes travelled over her face.

'The secret of my resounding success. Never let your right hand know what your left hand is doing!'

'How do you manage it?' she met his jewelled glance, colouring a little, and he regarded her quizzically for a moment. There was something strangely familiar about the whole thing. His crisp black hair with its deep natural wave clung to the shape of his head, the very definite moulded features bathed in sunlight. He had a very deep tan, so it wasn't business all the time, she thought, closing her hand with a little sigh. She was staring, but she didn't seem aware of it, and into his fine eyes came a sparkle of amusement.

'You're looking at me with all the careless concentration of a child. You wouldn't be trying to provoke me, would you, Gabriele?'

Something in his voice thoroughly disconcerted her.

'I've the notion I might have to sing for my supper!'

'But you're only a babe yet, otherwise, who knows? No, don't quiver. I promise you you'll regret nothing from now on. I'm a very gallant man, I think you should know. Or might you regret it, I wonder?'

She was forced to look at him, conscious of his mockery and amusement. 'You're like a small boy with a squirrel ...'

'Or is it the other way round?' A point of light danced in his eyes and she looked away again, with a quick loss of confidence.

'I would never contradict you,' she said, endearingly young. 'Neither do I want to quarrel.'

'Are we quarrelling? I thought we were being as affectionate as a niece with her uncle.'

'Just as I said ... a small boy with a squirrel.'

'I think we're both juggling words, but why? Words, the first line of defence. Warral Towers on the left. As you can see, it's convenient and I have a view from the top. Camilla does all the entertaining for Sir Joshua. What more could one want?'

'I'd be too young to know,' Gabriele said serenely, unable to resist it, but he suddenly pinned her wrist with his free hand, his narrowed eyes, like silver, ranging over her face.

'You couldn't leave that alone, could you?'

'No!' She gave a curious little shake of her head, but he didn't release her, his fingers locked round her wrist.

'Shame on you, Gabriele. You've got the rest of the evening to clear yourself. The game is mine, after all!'

If it was, it was just as well to retreat. She sank back into the pigskin upholstery, careful to keep quiet. Fencing with Kyle Tyson was very like taking the high jump when one scarcely knew whether the pool was full or not. A faint little pleat appeared on her smooth, curved brow. The whole situation gave her something to think about. Being the object of Kyle Tyson's attention might be a splendid state of affairs, but it was also confusing. He knew every trick there was for activating the imagination, until even the boundaries of her immediate environment seemed blurred and only the man himself had any dimension. Another one of his many talents, she supposed. She turned her head out the window, inspecting the soaring spire of water from one of the city's fountains. It rested her light, cool eyes, behind which a hundred and one complex emotions were blossoming like roses in the Elder Gardens. From almost anywhere in the city you could see the hills again, standing very close to the city. 'The enchanted hills', William Light, the first Surveyor-General had called them, and the city of Adelaide named after William IV's consort: 'A more beautiful spot can hardly be imagined ... with thousands of acres of the richest land I've ever seen ... a fine old English look!'

Many examples of Colonial architecture were to be found in the Adelaide hills, simple homesteads and the magnificent, rich men's mansions. Sundown. Vineyards too, and orchard country. Thousands of tons of apples and pears, cherries, apricots, peaches and strawberries, the soft fruit for local consumption, a great deal of the pome fruit for interstate and overseas market. At the foot of the ranges, south of the city, was the biggest concentration of almond orchards in the southern hemisphere, in late winter lighting up the plains with an exquisite pale rose radiance. There were farmlands too and rich dairy pasture, but no one could deny that the grape was king, centre of an industry of great commercial importance; the fabulous Barossa Valley and the Range where the German flavour was strong and proudly preserved by the descendants of the early Lutherans who settled there and gave to their tiny villages names like Krondorf and Gnadenfrei Schonborn and Kaiser-Stuhl. The Metropolitan vineyards and those of the foothills were planted and religiously cultivated by British hands, some of them still owned by direct descendants, the old wineries modernised.

Warral Towers, as she suspected, was a splendidly-sited, exclusive block of flats in the round, with each apartment granted the benefit of a view, and those on top, a fantasy land by night. It came as no surprise when they took the lift to the penthouse—indeed half of the top floor; Connor had to be accommodated, especially when he turned out to be a spare and extremely elegant old gentleman who summed Gabriele up at a shrewd glance, then smiled in a sudden pact of friendship. She was inside the very modern, rather futuristic apartment with Connor offering to look after her before delivering a few short aside messages to Kyle Tyson, who disposed of each one neatly with no show of surprise at all. Then he was gone.

After that, it was a period of peace and quiet, some of the excellent coffee she had been promised, some pleasant conversation with Connor that touched on nothing significant, the soul of discretion, then he withdrew, leaving her to the cushioned comfort of a suede-upholstered rocker armchair and some muted Stravinsky from the hi-fi equipment concealed in a whole wall of dark mahogany cabinets. Through the open door of the living–dining room, an enormous free-flowing space, she could see into what must have been his office; a custom-made desk in black lacquer, a bright chrome and black leather swivel chair, a wall of books and a rust-coloured sculptured rug to match the linen curtains.

Everything was very tailored and contemporary with a colour scheme of ambers and golds, a huge abstract on one wall, unusual light fittings and a custom-made sofa that faced the night-time view, upholstered in a geometric pattern. It was quite a step from the traditional beauty of Sundown, with its wealth of antiques, for apart from a tall and very striking copper and enamel sculpture of an eagle, there was nothing in the way of 'objects' to distract the eye from the streamlined and very modern furnishings. There was not the slightest doubt, either, that the apartment belonged to a man, and a highly individual one at that. There was no touch of a woman's hand, only the visual confrontation with the statement that a woman could add nothing in the way of interest or design. Or so she interpreted it, and she was not so very wrong. Kyle Tyson, whether he knew it or not, was basically hostile to women, for all his undoubted attraction. Now why was that so?

Intrigued, she embarked on just the smallest excursion to peep into his office. Even that had vitality, another dimension of the man himself. She lifted her eyes and met with a shock. A large and beautifully framed portrait, that looked straight across at her, over the desk. The woman wasn't young, neither was she strikingly handsome like her son, but she had his beautiful eyes— speaking eyes with a straight, lancing look, not without a tinge of mockery. The painting itself had a great deal of technical skill and panache, but a realistic quality as though the artist sought to give as accurate an account as possible of his subject with no attempt at flattery. The result was an uncanny, rather unnerving feeling of immediacy, as though the woman, clever and magnetic in life, could if she chose step out of the frame so one could better judge the cause of the fascination that had been hers.

'Oh!' involuntarily Gabriele stepped back, caught up in a funny little tide, a rare prickle along her nerves. This woman was trying to bridge the gulf between the past and herself. Against the dark blue background the face was blazingly alive, the more so the longer one looked at it, the silvery eyes alive with unblinking concentration.

It was hardly surprising in her young sensitivity and her own raw emotions that she should withdraw. She would dearly have loved to own such a portrait of her own mother, yet impulse, strange and irrational, sent her out of the room. She had much to learn, much to experience before she could converse with Rachael Tyson on her own level. On the outside balcony the sun was declining as she resumed her seat in the deeply upholstered armchair. Stravinsky melted into Prokofiev. *Visions fugitives*. She slid her hands along the soft suede arms of the chair, very still and relaxed. Only the music, to which she was very susceptible, was closing in on her, the warmth of the chair. She felt blissful, utterly secure, and she didn't have to bother to ring Sundown, which frankly she didn't want to do. An admission perhaps that had she a single spark of astuteness she would have run for home, like a child not allowed up too late. Ah well! ... She inhaled deeply. Sundown, Aunt Camilla, everything seemed too far removed to bother about. She particularly liked this sixth variation. Her right hand on the chair picked out the melodic line, *con eleganza*.

She was on a beach with the warm breeze tickling her closed eyelids. A fine spray off the surf bloomed her straight slender limbs. Her hair lifted in silvery wings. Overhead the sky arched as clear as blue-tinted glass. The sun dazzled the white sand. Fronds of a giant coconut palm waved above her, swishing musically. *Inquieto.* Enchantment. Gradually through her reverie Gabriele became aware of a leaf on her face, thrown by the breeze off the ocean. It landed somewhere between her eyes, feathering against the warm, polished skin. She put up her hand.

'And a good thing you woke up!'

The voice was low-pitched, black velvet and vibrant. She opened her eyes on changed landscape, yet it had happened before. In a book. In a picture. In a dream.

'It's all right!' he smiled, faintly ironical. Her face was oddly defenceless. 'Don't worry, Gabriele, waking or sleeping, you're instant grace. But snap out of it, you're still in that dream of yours. Can you get up?'

'I don't know!'

His eyes were crystal clear in a deep copper mask. 'You look a very fragile creature in that armchair. I don't believe a woman has ever lost herself in it before. Well?' His dark-timbred voice was very quiet and sane. He looked very alert and alive in the soft, golden light, but she seemed unable to cope, her smoky eyes enormous, half dazed.

'That was a bit of irresponsible timing on my part, wasn't it?' His voice was light but infinitely disturbing.

'I'm sorry. I shouldn't have fallen asleep.' Her voice was very soft, a little strained, and he smiled, a smile that sought to dispel a mood that was colouring his own.

'Come on, up. I think we should go!' He looked very adult and responsible, and here she was behaving so oddly. 'What is it?'

'Nothing! I just feel a little strange, that's all!'

'And why not?'

The silence, the sight of him, the shock of it was be-

yond anything she could withstand. Her nerves, strung
out to breaking point, flared up in a riot, loading the
atmosphere with a breathless tension. She felt a little
shiver pass over her body and the effect on him was
instantaneous. With a faultless, disciplined movement,
his hands over-gentle, he lifted her from the chair. The
light struck gold from her hair, glossed the high planes
of her brow and cheekbones, the frosted sheen of her
mouth, the iridescent eyes, huge and a little lost. Her oval
face had no smile. She was utterly serious, masking the
wild agitated leap of her heart. She was reacting now,
independent of will or logic, a flood of longing swept in
from nowhere, outside living memory.

'The one thing we cannot afford!' he said in suave
denial, steadying her with his hands. 'My quarrel with
women doesn't extend to you, Gabriele!'

Her throat seemed to close, her breathing quick and
disturbed like her accelerated heartbeats. 'My sweet
Gabriele,' he said flippantly, 'are you coming or not? I've
the decided notion you're leading me round in circles
and I'm very easily upset. Gabriele? ...' He shook her a
little, easy yet authoritative, and she closed her eyes to
blot out a sensation of spinning endlessly, endlessly out
into a starry void. His tall figure loomed over her, dark
and determined, his profile suffused with tawny gold—a
profile she could have drawn blindfold.

'This isn't a dream, this is reality. Open your eyes.'

'Not until I'm quite, quite sure!'

'Sure of what?'

She tried to frame an answer in the cool way that was
hers, but the words refused to come. His voice made her
head spin. To be seduced by a voice! So arrogant, so
self-sufficient, so *amused*, when she was filled with this
curious flame. Urgently she threw up her head and

looked at him, searching his dark face. She could hear the intake of his breath as if a whip flicked him. His eyes were lit silver, the vertical line of danger between his brows.

'The least comforting thing I know,' he said hardily, 'is that we never stop making fools of ourselves, and you're greatly too much. In that my judgment was astonishingly reliable!'

A sensual awareness spun out like a thread, linking them in a reckless kind of excitement. His lean hand came under her chin, lifting her head. The tips of his fingers touched the corner of her mouth and on a soft little impulse she turned her cheek into his hand. So simple. No fuss. Only a miracle. Like new life or a constellation of stars that swung out of their predestined place. Something of what she was feeling, the sensuous appeal, must have got through to him, for his hand encircled her white nape, shaping it, his fingers threading into her hair so that the silver-gilt coil came loose and fell over his wrist.

'Molten silver!' he said conversationally, as if nothing at all was happening. 'As beguiling as silk. There's always the point when one can turn back, and you haven't heeded it at all, Gabriele. Now there's two of us!'

She had not the power nor the wish to turn her head. His mouth came down on hers with a wild, sweet clamour, a mastery that brought her mouth alive in its own right, soft and very sweet, and had she known it quite terrifyingly passionate. He turned her fully into his arms, slender fragile bones gathered against his hard frame, aroused as a man by such flower-like unfolding, so that the piercing yearning became not unmixed with a little fear. So this was hunger, a slow, drowsy hunger that mounted to a flame she herself had incited. And no one to blame. Her white arms were locked about his neck, her ash-gold hair and her sensitive face thrown into sharp relief against his deeply tanned skin and crisply curling dark hair.

To have come so far down the road of physical excitement in such a short time—it didn't seem possible, yet it happened. It was happening now. Desire like an unfurling flower, the tight bud that sprang into full splendour ... He broke away from her, alienating himself, pulling her arms down.

'It's a decided advantage when one doesn't give a damn, but it just so happens I care. You're too young, too helpless, too charming. In short you represent a state of affairs too chaotic to be described!' His dark face, usually so vivid was now expressionless. 'Come on, let's go and eat!'

'Eat?' she sounded bewildered. 'But I've lost my appetite.'

'It will come back!' he hastily assured her, his light eyes sparkling. 'You're only young, for all you have a fleeting resemblance to the Sphinx—ageless with mysteries. God knows where you learnt them. In the cradle, one supposes. Come on,' he said briskly, 'one clean break and it's done!' He looked very tall and determined and there was nothing else to be done.

'I'd better fix my hair,' she said suddenly, sounding alarmed.

'You'll have to manage in the car. It would be sheer folly to go through that experience. Men are notoriously susceptible to long hair, and I refuse to stay here a moment longer.'

'It was your idea, after all!' she said, stung.

His expression, rather formidable, changed at the colour that swept under her skin. 'Ah yes, but I refuse point blank to accept the responsibility. Come along, Gabriele, a change of scene before you vanquish me entirely. I think I'll have a Chateaubriand, what about you?'

She didn't deign to reply because there was nothing she could say that would affect him one way or the other. Such splendid insolence, the original unabashed male, superior in every detail, all his own way and no complications. What a pity no one had yet come along to upset his schemes. If only she were older, wiser, a witty sophisticate like Aunt Camilla. As it was she was still trembling like a sapling swept by the storm.

At the door he turned and smiled at her with that vastly unfair charm. He held out his hand and she took it, an irresponsible teenager being taken out for a treat. What Appollonian benevolence! His head in fact had all the detached splendour of an old Greek coin. Gabriele continued to watch him in complete absorption, chin up, a flash of hostility in her smoky grey eyes.

He gave her an odd, amused glance. 'Tell me you're sorry for behaving so badly!'

'I'm sorry!' she said instantly. 'I always remember my manners. It won't happen again.'

'Well, smile at me, then,' he said compellingly. 'One kiss isn't the end of the world!'

'God forbid! Not at nineteen. That's too young to die.'

He looked down at her for a full five seconds, his deeply bronzed face quite bland, but the eyes mocked her. 'Women, you just can't trust them. I've discovered that to my horror. Honestly, Gabriele, you have everything—beauty, brains, charm, a kick like a small donkey for all the ribbons and bells, but I've no intention of succumbing. In fact I'm more wary than ever. But no power on earth is going to deprive me of that Chateaubriand and your company. Now if we're going at all, let's go. Unless you've other plans, we've wasted far too much time already!'

'*Indeed!*' she seconded very blithely, her normally serious and charming expression for once lively. What was falling utterly, irrevocably in love if not trivia? He would think so. What a complex fate it was to be a woman, incurably romantic. She might search the whole world over and not find another such as he, infinitely attractive for all his self-confessed hostilities. Not that it would do her the least bit of good, she was going to enjoy tonight. It was bravado, she was certain of that, but what did she care? This was her first taste of involvement and adventure and she was utterly thrown by it with no thought of the cost.

CHAPTER SIX

THE main drawback to Gabriele, Noel decided, was that
she took no pains to conceal her intelligence—one of the
biggest mistakes a woman ever made. It irked him, a
man like other men, ignoring as he did its deeper implica-
tions, he was not particularly intelligent himself, though
he would never have believed it, being a Narcissist to
the fingertips, obstinate, quick-tempered and self-con-
tradictory, but not without a certain facility in repartee
which usually earned him a place at Camilla's parties.
As well, he was quite decorative as slick, fair young men
go, for Camilla rarely troubled herself with those who
could not make an effort, a jewel of perfection herself.

For all his study of Gabriele tonight, Noel felt profoundly dejected. She looked quite beautifully elegant,
aloof, yet for all that completely feminine. A Grecian
nymph in her chastely clinging white gown, her long,
silky pale hair drawn back off her brow in a classical
style to reveal the fine modelling of her face and head.
She suggested a young woman both complex and delicate, and he could feel the exasperation of wanting her
all to himself. Strange, and he had to admit it, for he was
essentially antagonistic to her whole style. That cool
patrician look of hers suggested a certain independence
of spirit as if she had no need to proclaim her equality
to man when every man knew that was downright
laughable. Out of the question. The church, the bed, and
the kitchen—they couldn't aspire to much more than
that. Noel had a decided appreciation of the ridiculous
and the faintly bitter notion that all women at heart

were like his mother.

Across the swirling pattern of flowers and dresses, the luxurious furnishings, the priceless objets d'art, the soft brilliance of the twin chandeliers, he saw Gabriele smile at Kyle Tyson. *Tyson*, a black and white study in sombre elegance like the fallen angel himself. What malicious god had sent him hence? A shrill shock of jealousy ran through him. It tore out of him, striking him with a kind of self-horror—no mean feat, for Noel stood consistently high in his own regard. People were looking at him, so there was the immediate, nervous need to hide behind a mask. The smile, he told himself, was a mere social gesture. It was a smile one could never tire of, Noel thought, an eternal source of mystery and desire.

Women were the very devil! One might wish to God one could do without them. Was it possible he had become infatuated with a girl he didn't actually *like*? After all, she wasn't his type. Undeniably lovely in her white dress though she was, he much preferred Camilla's—a real stunner, a flame-coloured thing with a superb feather boa and such panache! Those were real diamonds that swung from Camilla's ears, matching the points of brilliance in those fabulous black eyes. Camilla was a work of art tonight, luscious as a peach bloomed to perfection, yet he continued to look after her niece. Gabriele with her fastidious delicacy!

Completely absorbed, it took him a few seconds to become aware of a pair of silvery grey eyes that were regarding him with a glitter of sardonic amusement. Noel smiled in an absurdly stilted way, feeling agonisingly transparent. He waved his champagne glass gaily, feeling the quick heat of being patronised. Did the man miss anything? The least little thing? It was as if he ran an extraordinarily elaborate and successful espionage system. Such perceptions were unnerving. The crisp black head turned back to Camilla again and Noel returned to his reflections. Gabriele—her face seemed to swim into his mind so often of late, especially in the hours after midnight. It wasn't love, certainly not. He didn't kid himself there. He liked a girl to do exactly what he might want, and Gabriele would never do that, but she attracted him fatally. There was no doubt of that, not after tonight. It seemed as if he had been at the party an eternity, and all because Gabriele had not said more than a dozen words to him. Nor to anyone much outside of Lynnton and that gave him much comfort. Certainly not Kyle Tyson, for all that silent, shared secrecy of the smile they exchanged.

Kyle Tyson, as ever, was one of Camilla's charmed circle, or more accurately, together they presented a smooth and sophisticated front as would lead an outsider to believe Kyle Tyson and not Paul Lynnton was the beauteous Camilla's consort. Paul Lynnton, for his part, did nothing to dispel the illusion—on the fringe for the most part, his old tawny-gold magnificence sadly dimmed, a drink never out of his faintly trembling hand. He had a problem there, Noel thought with waspish satisfaction, a social drinker himself, and enviably slim, and not a one of them there that didn't know it. From the look on his tawny flushed face, Gabriele or the drink or both were some compensation. Old Josh was said to be seething disgusted about his grandson. If all the old rumours were to be believed and Kyle Tyson and Paul Lynnton were linked by blood, there wasn't a single physical characteristic they had in common except perhaps that they were both over six feet. But Kyle Tyson was extravagantly classy, as lean as a thoroughbred, all fluid co-ordination and hard muscle, while Paul Lynnton had allowed the splendid physique of his youth to become ruined with an excess of drink and increasing indolence. In his Varsity days he had been considered a fine athlete. No sign of it now, neither could one hope for a happy ending, not with Camilla exulting in the best things in life.

Kyle Tyson's rise to power had been meteoric. There seemed no end to his skills and accomplishments, business and otherwise. No position to which he could not aspire. Camilla, it was certain, was ravished by those dark good looks, the startling contrast of light eyes, the way his hair grew; the force and the drive that all went to make up Kyle Tyson's personality. But what of Tyson? He had brought diplomacy into the power game, his social manner smooth and polished, witty and urban, faintly sardonic. Towards all Camilla's older women friends, he was equally attentive, leading, for one, Noel's mother astray. Many the time she had remarked with a pathetic passionate earnestness that Kyle Tyson had the great good sense and judgment to prefer the mature woman to any ten gauche girls. No woman in her forties was passée these days. On the contrary, the older women had everything to offer the more discerning male, which was probably true could they only see it. But not Mother. Camilla, now, might be a miracle of youth and beauty, but for his mother to imagine she was still in the running, which she did, was an impossible absurdity.

The thing was, Kyle Tyson was really a genuine phenomenon, Noel considered, a man who had made it to the top in a man's world, a battlefield with all those decisions to be the right ones, with women of all ages engulfing the sidelines, desperate for his attentions. He really should be made to tell! It must be the infernal tilt of his head, the careless arrogance, the voice and manner that bespoke a long tradition of ease and affluence. Actually, from all accounts, he had been something of a firebrand, a real troubleshooter in his teens. Well, the angry young man had settled down. There was no rashness there, only a sure confidence in his ability to accomplish whatever he wanted and no conjuring tricks on the side.

Sickened and envious, Noel felt a desperate need for action of some kind. His tactics with Gabriele were at fault. He could see that now. Basically she was tediously strait-laced. Public relations was his job, after all. He was expert in putting up a front. He could, if he chose, create the right atmosphere with this maddeningly aloof girl—an impossible vision tonight. She reminded him of something gliding across that beautiful room, humming with laughter and conversation, the muted background music of a group that had been hired for dancing out on the terrace. Camilla's parties never went through the initial warming-up process. They sparkled right from the moment of arrival like the champagne that flowed like water. Not domestic either! No one could call Camilla stingy. Her suppers as well were never less than sumptuous, not that Noel much indulged in them. He had a horror of putting on weight which would completely spoil his boyish image and his clothes fitted him exactly.

'Gabriele!' In his haste he nearly upset a leaf of a gorgeous eighteenth-century chinoiserie screen, all flowers and plants and exotic birds. 'Bother!' his nerves shrieked at him. Flushed and embarrassed, he steadied it with his hand. A few had broken off in their conversations to turn to look at him. Had the screen come down it would have hit a jade carving of the phoenix and the dragon. No doubt Mother had seized on his rare burst of clumsiness. He would hear of it again. How mortified she was! It was all Gabriele's fault in any case. He had the humiliating impression that she was making an attempt to get away from him or at least bracing herself against a magnificent Georgian chair. But he wasn't going to be put off. Faint heart never won fair lady, or any other kind.

His hummingbird flight made up for his bad moment. In an instant he was beside her, catching her bare arm. 'Manners! I thought you were going to cut out on me!'

'Not at all.'

'Well then!' said Noel, looking around brightly, trying to cover this sheer uprush of physical pleasure. Close to he couldn't take his eyes off her, the flawless skin of her face and long throat, the white sloping shoulders, the shadowed cleft of her breast. A white swan, that was it! That regal but quite natural aloof look that fascinated him as much as it annoyed and made him uncomfortable. All the same, she would make a very radiant ornament for a man's home. A woman who looked and talked like an angel. He could do a lot worse and her background was impeccable. The more he thought about it the more convinced he had become. It was about time he took a wife. Nothing could be worse than life with Mother of late. She who had lashed him with her tongue since he found wit to resist. That was when she wasn't swinging to perverse extremes buying him the most expensive items of wearing apparel. Of course his image helped her own. There was always method in a woman's madness.

'Let's grab a pew!'

An Irish love-seat upholstered in velvet did just as well. It was set back in an alcove, for one thing. Noel settled back happily and slid his arm along the back of the seat, bringing all his abilities to bear on the task of charming Gabriele—so much so that for the next ten minutes she quite succeeded in liking him. Dancers came back in from the terrace and across the room a spirited and amiable argument broke out interspersed with Camilla's throaty three-noted laughter and Kyle Tyson's dark, distinctive voice, with a faint edge to it.

'Outrageous, isn't it?' Noel said on one of the vengeful impulses he had inherited from his mother.

'What is?' Her face and her voice were quite cool and composed, but he felt a great certainty.

'Well, really, sweetie, look at Camilla. She shrieks it to the skies!'

'You're very warm in your friendships!' Gabriele said cuttingly, and he flushed.

'Delightfully easy-going too, so don't get angry. I know Camilla's your aunt, but allow me to stress the purity of my motives. I like to get at the truth. No sham. Mark you,' he added reasonably, 'I see nothing wrong with anyone getting a bit of fun out of life. I can't say I admire her taste.'

'You're rather extraordinary, aren't you?' said Gabriele. 'Such tact. Such loyalty. A guest in this house, and to choose this precise moment . . .'

'A dilemma won't go away just because you like to bury your head in the sand. Actually, old thing, I don't anticipate there'll be any difficulties at all once the old man's gone. He's dead against any scandal. Like all wicked old birds he's agin it in anyone else. Don't do as I do, and so forth!' He looked at her closely. 'I seem to annoy you, but why? What has decided you against listening to some inside information? I'm not looking to upset you and really we're all involved in this thing. Not deeply, to be sure, but somewhat!'

'My only wish at the moment, Noel, is to perpetuate the charmed atmosphere of this party.'

'Well, naturally, sweetie.'

'You're making that difficult!'

'Be that as it may, I'm determined you'll hear me out. A hard lesson is never forgotten. Of course, in a way you can't blame Camilla. He's very positive and grand, our Tyson, surrounded by the whole apparatus of power. Naturally he would appeal to her. She'd have no time at all for failures.'

'And Uncle Paul is?' she asked in a disquieting voice.

'The truth is often painful, isn't it? It's not a bit of use despising me. I'm not despicable at all. I'm your friend. It's in your own interests, after all. You just could be in the house when the storm breaks.'

'I don't think there's one chance in ten million of what you're hinting at!'

'Oh no?'

'Could it be you're just caught up in a maelstrom of gossip. It always surrounds people like Aunt Camilla and Kyle Tyson. They're not quite like the rest of us.'

'No indeed! Point taken, though I imagine Lynnton finds that rather irrelevant. I admire loyalty, sweetie, but within reason. *Within reason*. Camilla, if she so chose, could destroy her husband. What is he? Just look at him now—listless, a puppet figure, a cipher, a glass never out of his hand. If one lives for the drink, one will very largely die from it,' Noel said with great conviction, being a non-drinker, addicted to cigarettes.

Gabriele avoided his bright hazel eyes. Thoughts she had wearied over and over persistently in the back of her mind now suddenly resolved themselves. She shivered as if she had just realised she had gone quite mad. There were so many reasons against feeling the way she had done for the past few days, but reasons never had the power and pull of feeling. Her eyes moved to her Aunt Camilla weighing her strengths. What weaknesses she had were certainly not apparent. She looked a glorious creature, beside whom most women would fall into insignificance. Indeed, those of her friends vain enough took care not to stand too close beside her for fear of comparisons. She drew the eye as naturally, as irresistibly as a flame, in a gown only she would dare. Her slim, seductive body was half turned towards Kyle Tyson, so vivid and mocking, undeniably amused by something she had said. He was no closer to her than half a dozen men, yet by some odd trick it seemed as though they were intent on each other, as if no one else existed in that gay, ever-changing circle around them. Some powerful emotion moved in Gabriele against which she was helpless. Her heart cried and over a passionate protest, but she was so essentially honest she knew she had no rights in the affair. No one really belonged to anyone else, only themselves. At her side, Noel too seemed to have slumped into a decline under the burden of his own painful experiences too numerous to mention. She felt ill herself as though she had blundered into some violence, but Noel was simmering with ingrained resentments, quite a different thing.

'This could all be supposition,' she said, deeply disturbed.

'My sweet girl, I have a bulwark of unassailable facts.'

'None of my business in any case,' she said quickly, 'so please don't parade them for me. I must make it clear you do Uncle Paul a grave injustice. He is *not* fundamentally weak, be sure of it. He's going through an unhappy period of his life where he lacks the will and the inclination to really do something about his situation.'

'You're criticising, darling!' Noel pointed out maliciously.

'I suppose I am. I hope it's constructive, for I would dearly like to help him. He's been very kind to me and I love the children. Melissa has my own mother's eyes, right to the expression. She's the dearest little girl. Both the children worry about their father. I know Aunt Camilla is different, but she's a most remarkable woman.'

'After her fashion! You don't like her, do you, but admirable girl, you're hiding it.'

'I see no point in rewarding your curiosity! If you don't mind, Noel . . .' She was on the point of rising, but he caught her hand.

'Gently, gently! Don't go, sweetie, you'll make it so blatant. Whose side are you on anyway? Don't tell me you're like the rest of them, lost your head and gone all mushy over Tyson?' He could feel the resistance in her, the swift disdain and withdrawal, and he patted her unresponsive hand. 'Look, I'm sorry, sweetie, I don't mean that at all. You've too much sense. I'm doing this badly. If you only knew, I'm as upset as you are. I've some fondness for old Paul myself. Take Tyson now, once he turns his massive energies towards something— well, my God! watch out. He's suave as all hell tonight, but at the office he's quite a different person—formidable, tough and demanding. He'll put all our heads on the block and no sending out for a swordsman, he'll do it himself. It's a known fact Lynnton is on the outer and Tyson is in. Of course old Josh sired him!'

'Naturally you'd believe that without a word from Sir Joshua or anyone else. You're really in possession of an astonishing number of facts available to no one else. I can't help feeling you're wasted, Noel. Have you ever considered going over to the other side?' She was treacherously near tears and the thought of it dismayed her. Wild almond colour flooded her white skin, and her eyes shimmered like lakes.

A statue come to life, he thought bitterly, in a fine blaze and incredibly beautiful. God help her, for Camilla would never be kind. 'A strike home!' he said flatly, and the muscles jerked in his face. 'I'm sorry, I didn't know. Apparently your taste too needs improving. What a fool you are, sweetie, and here I was thinking what an intelligent girl. If you want to save yourself heartache and a whole lot of unpleasantness don't invade Camilla's territory. She's ruthless, with precious few scruples either. You can forget the niece business. It won't help at all.'

Heads down, neither of them viewed the progress across the room of an interested observer.

'Whatever could you be discussing that could account for the tormented expressions?' a dark voice asked gracefully. 'Gabriele, I've hardly seen you all evening!'

She wouldn't look up at him, but she could feel the light, remarkable eyes on her. Noel, traitor that he was, had already concocted a frivolous answer, laughing nervously, on his feet, more double-dealing than ever. Why didn't he just fall down at the great man's feet? She never heard a word of their slender conversation, but trembled visibly when a lean, strong hand reached down and brought her to her feet. Force, for all it looked like a balletic movement.

'Charming to see a woman so demure,' he drawled, 'but you may look at me, Gabriele. Excuse us, Noel!'

He was propelling her through the crowded room out on to the rose and gold glow of the terrace with Noel's eyes like an assassin's dagger between his broad shoulder-blades. He was well aware of Noel and his sundry treacheries, but he wasn't ready to move yet, if ever. Time would pronounce a judgment on Noel Danton, and he had got off to a bad start with that mother of his. One had to make allowances for a staff member. So many things warped one through life and mothers of only sons were notorious, especially one as neurotic as Denise Danton. He had been studiously avoiding her for the best part of the evening, something difficult enough even for him, a recognised fast mover.

'I do believe Danton has a tenderness for you,' he said pleasantly to Gabriele's silver-sheened, averted head.

'How could you wish that on me?'

He laughed beneath his breath. 'Now you, Gabriele, I'd taken for a genuinely sweet young woman. What has Noel said to offend more, anger and bewilder you? Am I to hear or am I too deeply involved? If you tilt your head any further away from me, it will snap off. Come, let's dance and forget it. Noel has actually missed his calling. He's an incorrigible conspirator, but I've no mind for his head!' His voice, low and ironical, suddenly veered towards faint masculine impatience. 'What is this mad obstinacy, Gabriele? Look at me!' He didn't even wait for her compliance but lifted his hand. 'Tears? God, what next? I've said I've no mind for his head, but I've not the least objection to breaking his neck!'

Her young face held a peculiar sensitivity, a sharp kind of melancholy he couldn't fail to recognise. She was standing quite still and passive under his hand, staring out at an enormous cape jasmine, an unearthly white radiance in the moonlight, its perfume on the night air unbearably sweet. At the far end of the terrace, shadows deepened, languorous, beckoning, luxuriously indolent. Her pale hair clasped her head like silver. Flesh, bone, every nerve ending was responding to the touch of his hand on her bare skin. The stir and challenge of a man who did not need a woman to lead him. Anywhere.

He made a faint sound of masculine impatience as he looked down at her, her aura of melancholy and wistfulness like a Botticelli Madonna that made him want to comfort her as much as shake her conflicting sentiments, and powerful ones at that, so that, provoked, he swung her very directly into his arms.

'I can see my offers of action are worth nothing, so let's dance!' Demanding, expecting, her instant yielding to his encircling arm.

Such was his effect on her, she did, melting swiftly against him with her delicate body, her eyes mirror-bright but free now of all desire to weep. Vivid, audacious, he looked undisputed master of every situation, certainly in command of any form of resistance she might offer, and she was about to offer none. The door had swung shut on all counter-moves. It was there in his touch again, not just the fantastic sensuality, but the strong feeling of reassurance as from that very first handshake; the protective quality she evidently aroused in him against his inclinations. And was that all? She knew only the powerful urge to be in his arms again, to touch and be touched by him, all her emotions firing in a quick chain reaction.

He looked down at her, fully aware of her yielding, and his smile was very white and sardonic in his tanned face. 'Some music moves in you, Gabriele, for all I'd like to give you a good shaking!'

'Would you explain it?' she asked, not wanting to cross him at all.

'Does it matter how? Who taught you to dance like this anyway? I might have expected it. There's a devil of a strength in a woman's softness alone.'

She too had become aware that they had found a

perfect rhythm, almost unbidden, so that every physical movement was in splendid accord. Her face reflected a passionate seriousness, the impulse of the heart and mind to take these few moments and lock them away for ever so no one could get them. She knew so little about him, only that she loved him and trusted him, though heaven knew why, and she had to be grateful for what little time she got.

'You look faintly sad!' his voice mocked her, his cheek hazed her hair.

'I'm always sad about things I can't understand!'

Kyle didn't say any more but only laughed beneath his breath, gathering her slight femininity against him, as fresh and delicate as a flower. The whole length of the terrace was before them, suspended in a glittery calm. How in the world had she passed in a few moments from a toppled world and forced-on-her premonitions to this softest, most irresistible excitement? Her hand lay on the beautiful black cloth of his jacket, very pale and austere, slender, oval-tipped fingers. Swiftly she turned up her head as if at a signal and caught the amused sheen of his gaze. Memories like drowned jewels shimmered out of her eyes. Lightly they touched the curve of his mouth, then she looked away again at the blossoming formal garden, the dark outline of the hills.

'I've missed you!' he said dryly.

'And I you. A calm and undramatic statement of truth!'

'Naturally!' He smiled again, his eyes on her cool gentleness. Gabriele had almost forgotten where they were. They might have been quite alone in that star-spangled night, the music slowed to a love-dance, ageless, borne on the wind, not played by human hands at all. She wasn't conscious of the other dancers that brushed by them, nor did she see the curious and sometimes openly avid glances directed at them from within and without. Not Noel, stationed stiff-backed by the French doors, white hatred in his heart and a smile on his face. Her every perception was given over to a whole catalyst of emotions magnified like her heartbeats. Yet she had this odd sense of homecoming, almost as if she had always known his touch for all its unique strangeness and excitement. She had come a long, long way in the process of self-development, but she still had a long way to go. She gave the faintest little sigh of pleasure, her breath moving the lovely clinging bodice of her gown. Her expression relaxed into one of pure enchantment, so simple to read—and he wasn't blind. Far from it. But it couldn't be helped. Time to don helmet and armour later. Not for anything could Gabriele have protected herself then or pretended a sophistication far beyond her means.

Kyle's hand, very subtle on her bare skin, seemed to harden disturbingly, yet there was no increased pressure at all, just a feeling. The wild colour came up under her skin and she stumbled a little without warning so that he chided her lightly, catching her closer into his arms. Even the scented darkness at the far end of the terrace seemed to be shaking. Or were her heartbeats shaking her? She blinked her eyes, trying to gather her resources, but only succeeded in looking oddly defenceless and quite mysteriously luring him on.

He looked down into the heightened beauty of her face, the pearlescent skin in the soft gloom.

'From an ethereal apparition to *this*!' he said in a low drawl. 'It seems an intolerable thing when the immediate need is for caution. For such an innocent you can wreak a tremendous amount of havoc, Gabriele. You seem to have hit on the essence of femininity—and all at nineteen! It's difficult indeed not to just pick you up and make love to you.'

'But you *are*, aren't you?' she asked, her voice hushed, for him alone.

'There's no certainty about anything, my lamb!' he countered very suavely.

'I could mourn for myself if that's the case!'

He looked immensely vital and quite dangerous, and it gave her a moment of wry humour. They weren't matched at all.

'Most men have an appetite for beauty!' he suggested lightly.

'But you like me, don't you? I mean, you really do like me as a person. Not a woman at all!'

'Oh, don't be absurd!' He gave a low, vibrant laugh and tightened his hold on her narrow waist. 'Now's the time to move!'

'But it wasn't meant to be funny at all!'

'The funniest things often aren't!'

She looked up at his handsome dark face and found it amused. Then they were out of the shadows, he all-conquering male, she so weak and wavering, but these moments had a shattering sweetness about them rarely found. Gabriele wasn't so young and inexperienced that she didn't know that. If she had to pay and pay dearly, she decided there and then, it was well worth it. There seemed no perfect existence away from him. His silvery eyes might be full of a lazy impudence, but his body was moving differently—a pas de deux, perfect in itself, the ideal. Her beauty was as luminous as a pearl, lit by a steady glow, very sure against a midnight blue ground.

He didn't seem inclined to talk either as if he too shared her pleasure. What differences that lay between them were for the moment subdued. They looked, had

they known it, a striking visual impression of man
woman; a complementary and brilliant physical repre-
sentation as natural and beautiful as day and night
Serene femininity, delicate and graceful, the gentleness
of contour against harsher male beauty and grace—a
sight that was only very occasionally greeted with whole-
hearted pleasure. More, with jealousy and envy, a few
at least, furious and one with shocked incredulity as if
an impregnable fortress was being invaded.

Kyle, glancing over Gabriele's head briefly, caught
Noel Danton's fleeting expression. A mind far less acute
than his own would have immediately seized on the
implication that Noel was gazing at a spectacle both
decadent and smouldering with primitive passions. He
Kyle Tyson, was no less than a ravening monster, a
satyr with a chaste Grecian maiden trapped in his
arms. He almost laughed aloud.

Gabriele felt the faint tremor of laughter and murmured, her voice still muted with dreamy pleasure, the
intense awareness so recently acquired.

'What is it? What's amusing you?'

'Danton's face, if you must know, little one. What was
it he said to you? You'd best tell me. You will some
time or other.'

'I can't bring myself to tell you at all.'

'You must learn not to disobey me. Why can't you?
Are you afraid?'

'Yes. A little!'

'Ah!' he gave a long-drawn-out sigh, his taut silvery
gaze on the sky. 'I can imagine. A sense of charity is
rarely found in persons as insecure and unhappy as
Noel Danton. You might remember that, Gabriele.'

'Do you imagine I believe everything I hear?' she
challenged him, wondering where all this was leading.

'What have you heard, then? And now, Gabriele, to answer your question, I know you rather well, I think. You'd be scrupulously fair to the point of being mistaken.'

'Well then, it's quite unimportant, isn't it? You have a marvellous, abrasive faculty for putting things in perspective!'

'Even so, I don't like secrets, little one.'

'And I'm essentially secretive!' She looked back at him, her eyes enormous, shimmering in her oval face.

'You're not!' he flatly contradicted her.

'I'm a woman!' she persisted.

'It's simply not necessary to point that out. I have twenty-twenty vision. Not that I actually need it so far as you're concerned. You're trying successfully to mesmerize me. Now why? I've told you before, you're too young—much too young. Nineteen going on five thousand or so.'

'It puzzles me why you're so antagonistic to women.'

'Am I?' His slight smile was mocking, his glance travelling over her face and throat as though it pleased his eye at least.

'You are and you know it, and it's so unfair. The world is chock full of wonderfully good women with every attribute imaginable!'

'Is that so?' he challenged her lazily. 'I've been around it until I'm dizzy and I haven't found the right one yet!'

'There must have been at least one serious candidate,' she insisted.

'You're exaggerating, Gabriele.'

'For once tell the truth! You said yourself you can trust me.'

'Did I really say that? What you ask, little one, is actually impossible, but I don't expect you to fully appreciate that!'

'Well, I'm suitably diminished by your steely regard, at any rate. It must be invaluable at Board meetings. I apologise if I seem to be prying. I remember now you told me your closeness is notorious.'

'It is among my distinguishing traits, yes. However, because I do like you and I do trust you in as much as I trust any woman I promise to tell you immediately I come up with a find!'

'You don't need to sound quite so defeatist about it! The first gust of wind might sweep her into your arms.' As she said it, the playful night breeze suddenly lifted a silky strand of her hair and skeined it across his face.

'More spells, little one!' he asked lightly, and her eyes, wide and startled, flew to his face. 'You're much better off out of it, Gabriele.'

'For which I have no possible answer at all. Thank you, anyway. That was the most perfect dance of my life. I won't spoil anything by saying I've rarely danced in my life. I've been far too busy studying and so forth!'

'You just could land yourself in a contretemps now,' he suggested.

'Oh, don't be angry, I was just borrowing a little of your own style,' she smiled.

'I'm not angry, but I'll remember, you'll find. Insubordination on every hand—here comes Noel!' Kyle turned his dark head, all arrogance, a big boss to not even a little boss. 'A most anxious and unsubtle observer. What a pity, when I was just about to ask you in to supper!'

'But Aunt Camilla . . .!' Gabriele cried before she could stop herself. She had no thought at all for any kind of insinuation, merely a most complete acceptance of the fact that Camilla would not sacrifice his presence on any account, least of all for her own niece, who really had no consequence in the scheme of things.

Kyle was hurting her of all things, his fingers biting into her wrist. She would have a bruise there tomorrow. His dark, handsome face was straight out of a legend—arrogance and challenge, his expression making one of its lightning transitions from amusement and mocking charm to hardness and force, full of tremendous vigour, quite ruthless. There, she'd said it, and seeing it she quailed, touching the tip of her tongue to her soft mouth. 'I'm sorry. Must I spend the rest of the evening apologising? What I really meant was I should feel mortally offended and neglected if you failed to take me in.'

His light eyes searched her face and his searing grasp relented. 'You know, Gabriele, it occurs to me you'll make quite a woman. Without outside help. Hello there, Noel,' he turned to the other man, suavely dismissive. 'I expect you've come to tell us supper is on. Gabriele is starving, aren't you, little one? Well, come along, then, while I've still strength enough to battle my way in!'

CHAPTER SEVEN

ALL down the path past the camellia house, exquisite
little flowering bulbs showed their faces above the cracks
in the natural rock; white and mauve alyssum, dwarf gar-
denias, fragrant and creamy, blue daisies and where the
path widened masses and masses of thickly growing
gazanias, their pert daisy faces showing at least twenty
colours, wide awake at barely half past six. The little
footpath beyond the glass orchid house received very
little traffic, the children using an easier slope down to
the vineyard. Ivy geraniums trailed right across Gabriele's
path, making it difficult for her to tread without crushing
their soft, petal pink blossom.

It was a beautiful morning, birds warbling, the earth
stirring with its special sweet freshness, and she had
awakened early feeling the great need to be out of doors,
alone, private with her own thoughts. It was necessary to
catch up with herself. The past few weeks had spun
away from her in a mad whirl, a kaleidoscope of parties
and non-stop chatter. Of course there were always
parties before Christmas, even at home, but Sundown
of all resembled a grand hotel full of strange tourists,
walking in at all hours of the day with small intimate
dinner parties to large functions going on every other
night.

Aunt Camilla thrived on it, glowed and grew even
more beautiful, except for the one morning when she
had come down at about eleven o'clock absolutely
'savage', as Melissa put it, because she had slept on her

face and left a bad crease in her magnolia skin. Mercifully for all of them, it had faded by nightfall and Camilla was herself again, very sweet and terribly preoccupied, very much the society hostess, so that Gabriele found herself supervising the children's tea; the bath hour; a little television—each child had a portable set drawn up to the end of their beds—then lights out about half past eight. She couldn't have cared less what time she went downstairs herself. Noel was sure to be there lying in wait like a tiger out on a limb. Somehow Aunt Camilla had convinced herself as well as everyone else within earshot that a romance was blossoming between her niece and the son of one of her dearest friends.

Last night's party Gabriele had escaped altogether, retiring soon after the children, all three of them having watched an old episode of *The Persuaders* perched on Melissa's bed. She truly did have a fearful headache, abandoned for the space of an hour, then it was there again, occasioned perhaps by Noel's proposal of marriage that same afternoon, terrifyingly backed up by his mother, who had given the whole thing her approval. For once Gabriele had been less tactful. She wasn't yet twenty—just a child! She was only on holiday with no thought of romance. She didn't in any case love Noel in the least. And she had every intention of finishing her arts degree.

Noel wasn't worried. Only a miracle could prevent her from loving him. She just needed more time. An engagement, before she changed over to his own glorious name. With an unwonted fire in his voice he couldn't see how she could be so horribly cruel as to turn him down. He had her aunt Camilla's backing, which was the great thing, and Gabriele had been dining and wining and sightseeing and sailing with him, all under Aunt Camilla's heavy persuasion. 'We can't afford our dearest friends, darling!'

Gabriele gave a little sigh, grateful for the cool morning breeze against her skin. Of Kyle Tyson she had seen very little, but then neither had anyone else, and she took heart from it whether it was foolish or not. He was an impossible dream, there was no doubt about that, but she like everyone else had a right to her dreams. From Paul Lynnton she had learnt that he was interstate with Sir Joshua, who was said to have suffered a slight setback, although no one had found the temerity to suggest he should take to his bed. Everyone appeared to go in awe of Sir Joshua, including his own grandson, who was full of a wry envy and admiration for Kyle Tyson, his fellow Director and Chairman of the Executive Council for the Lynnton Organisation. In Paul's opinion, Kyle Tyson was the only one outside of Sir Joshua who could restore order to the 'madhouse' which was what he called the hierarchy or executive offices on the top floor of a city building belonging to Sir Joshua and housing his interests.

Paul had shown Gabriele over them the previous week before taking her out to lunch at a smart restaurant. She had been impressed with the overall design, functional certainly, but luxurious, the high-key simplicity of the board room with its long mahogany and steel table, dark brown suede-covered swivel chairs, two large striking abstracts which irresistibly evoked the Centre, hot colours, bright ochres; an ocelot-patterned carpet and dull gold raw silk at the enormous plate glass windows overlooking the city. Each member of the executive group had been allowed a little individuality within the overall image which was, to Gabriele's eye, authoritative male. It hadn't needed Paul to tell her Kyle Tyson had

had several interviews with the firm responsible for the interior design. It seemed he disliked the woman's touch, at least in the home and in the office, and saying this Gabriele had made Paul smile. Kyle's attractiveness to women was as fabled as his allergy to marriage.

Paul himself was no longer 'Uncle' but a very likeable companion Gabriele still regarded as a close relative. If he was unhappy, which he was, he was rarely vocal about it. Whether he wished it or not, he loved his wife and adored his children, though it was Gabriele who always made up the group when he took them all out at the weekends. Aunt Camilla was never available for the beach or picnicking, and in any case the sun was disastrous for the skin. In the end, Gabriele and the children, firm friends, had lovely tans, though Paul insisted on watching them from the shade, being none too keen on any physical exertion which would have done him the world of good, as his young son was forever telling him. But she couldn't worry about Paul, Gabriele thought, she had problems of her own.

Slightly ahead of her down the verdant track, who should shoot out of the bushes but Lucrezia, the children's smoky Persian. Her large copper eyes were enormous with anxiety at the unaccustomed noise on the path, then she quietened, recognising a familiar. Passionately fond of caresses when it suited her, she waited, her great mystical eyes like a goddess, which she was a few thousand years back, swishing her short smoky tail, standing delicately on her blue paws.

'Oh, you beautiful creature!' Gabriele swept her up, suitably gentle and adoring. 'Pure white underneath, a blue, silver-shaded coat, long and thick and silky. A silver breast and silver ears. What could be sweeter—and you're not about to make a scene!' She stroked the delicate ears back against the round, wide head listening to the contented purring. From her vantage point she could see, running down the slopes in perpendicular rows, the vines. To the right the shy bearer, the Cabernet Sauvignon, the traditional quality red grape from Bordeaux. To the left, the luxuriant, more prolific Shiraz which produced a wine deeper in colour and more full-bodied with plenty of flavour. The estate produced two styles. The straight Cabernet and a blend, a small quantity of Cabernet to the heavier Shiraz which still possessed the quality of allowing the lighter, more delicate Cabernet to come through. Both styles were labelled either full-bodied or light dry red and showed the varietal name of the grape, for Sundown had discarded the misleading burgundy and claret in relation to Australian wines. Last year's Shiraz had been excellent, with the Cabernet deserving to be laid down for at least five years. A *cru classé*, comparable with the fine dry reds of Saint Emilion and Medoc Pomerol if not a Chateau Lafitte-Rothschild, or so Aunt Camilla said, and she was something of an authority.

Gabriele didn't know a great deal about wine, but she was learning. She knew it had four basic characteristics; appearance, bouquet, flavour and finish, and she had come to appreciate the appearance of the different wines through the beautiful glasses that were used at dinner, always clear and always suitable for the serving of wine. Variations of the short-stemmed tulip, a perfect combination of size, shape and thinness. Wide-mouthed glasses which allowed the bouquet of the wine to dissipate were never used at Sundown, which took its wines very seriously indeed, and none more so than Aunt Camilla.

By the time Gabriele reached the first line of vines,

Lucrezia had deserted her for something that flickered its tail and Gabriele moved happily down the dead straight rows, bending her ash-gold head now and then to examine the ripening berry clusters. All the growing things around the estate fascinated her and gave her great pleasure—the trees and the shrubs and the flowers, the great sweeps of lawn, the fruit orchards and the exotic and sometimes downright sinister orchids, but most of all, *vitis vinifera*, the sacred vine, revered in the ancient world from whence it had come.

Towards the end of summer, February probably, these green clusters would be magnificent bunches brought in from all parts of the vineyard for testing, for on the measure of the acid and sugar content was based the decision to pick. The spring rains had been adequate, summer was hot but not too fierce to affect quality, so what more could they want? Unconsciously Gabriele plucked off a hard berry and tried to press it between her fingers, imagining how it would look purplish plump with a loving bloom on it. It would be wonderful to be at Sundown for the picking when the itinerant workers laboured from daylight to dusk, filling their baskets for loading on to the trucks and the short trip to the winery.

Silent, visualising the cool morning scene bright with colour, the clamour of vintage time, she nearly jumped out of her skin when a harsh, dictatorial voice assaulted her.

'I say there, what the devil are you up to, girlie?'

Severe as an avenging deity, a venerable figure was making it briskly down the track as if the berry in her hand was the emerald eye of an idol. An ornamental crown of healthy green vine leaves sat round his silver tufted brow, a note neither of them appeared to find incongruous.

'What about yourself?' she challenged him, taking the war right into his camp. 'Where did you get those from?' she pointed to his crown. 'I can see by your clothes you're not Caesar or anyone.'

'The devil I am!' He came up beside her, not even puffing, though he must have been well past eighty, but like some old people he had gone young again. A bare, brown torso, sprinkled with freckles, flat open sandals on unmarked feet, beach baggies reaching down to his boyish knees. 'And who might you be?' he challenged her in the same manner, his eyes as curious as her own. 'Not Cleopatra, with that kind of hair!'

'Gabriele. Gabriele Somerville,' she said, and held out her hand. 'How are you, Sir Joshua?'

'Bother!' he barked at her, disappointed. 'Now how did you arrive at that conclusion?' he asked her, and shot from under still black, beetling brows the same flashing remnants of great dynamism that had alerted her in the first place.

'Not so difficult!' she smiled at him. 'One gets to create an aura, I imagine. Anyway, you looked very exalted swinging along there, certainly not one of our gardeners.'

'So, Gabriele, not as angelic as you look, I've heard about you,' he said, daring her to deny the lot of it.

'From whom?'

'Kyle. Who else?'

Just the sound of his name was like lights flashing about her. How wondrous strange! 'For better or worse I think I'm in love with him,' she said in an odd little voice, then jerked her head up, stiffening, startled as if struck. 'Now how in the world did I come to say that? I just can't believe it!'

'You did, and obviously meant it,' he said, much interested. 'Very occasionally in life we come out with what we're really thinking and feeling.'

'Certainly I never *meant* to say it. It can't be true anyway!'

'And now you're going to deny it!' he said, scornful. 'Be like everyone else, satisfy the conventions. Hide your secrets. They're safe with me in any case. One doesn't reach my age without a few surprising confidences. Most of the time we keep the things closest to us to ourselves. I'm no different. Why shouldn't you love him in any case? He's all a man should be. You'd be mad if you didn't!'

'I scarcely know him!' she protested over the small disgusted sound he made. 'Isn't love at first sight rather a joke?'

'You've proved it—rather empirically I'd say. Shakespeare said it all for us, in any case. Sometimes I think he said the lot.'

'Perhaps Blake said it just as well. Never seek to tell thy love, Love that never told can be.'

'You're not telling him. You're telling me,' he pointed out astringently.

'What an odd conversation we're having!'

'Not odd at all. You disappoint me, child. We're having a perfectly serious, utterly truthful conversation —that's what's odd about it. For someone of my temperament, love would not be possible if it didn't happen at first sight. Given another chance I'd change my mind. I've only loved two women in my life, in any case. One was my poor, downtrodden little mother, so hardworking and selfless. I loathed my father. An upstart and a bully!'

'Oh dear!' she said inadequately, seeing the life flash

out of his still dark eyes. No hardening of the arteries there.

'And that says it all. It's very important to have the right parents. Half of our troubles begin there. When you're a mother remember my words. I've never forgotten my childhood or how hard it was. Never did me all that much harm, I suppose. Look at that grandson of mine. Had it easy all his life. Too easy! My God, now he can't get off the giddy merry-go-round. A bitter disappointment to me, is my grandson.'

'He knows this and it hurts him, Sir Joshua!'

'Championing him, are you?' he shot at her. 'I don't need a damn woman to hide behind her skirts. Does he do a damn thing about it? *No!* The business would soon fall apart like a kingdom if Kyle was like Paul. One must have the right heir, clever and strong.'

'Paul is your grandson!' she said very quietly, and got impatient contempt for her trouble.

'Don't provoke me, Missy, with your rainwater eyes. If Paul thinks he's going to inherit all I've slaved to build up, he's got another think coming. He's not man enough to take his own wife in hand, let alone his life. He's out of the running!'

'It's none of my business in any case!' said Gabriele, hurt and upset for Paul. Why didn't he shake himself out of the miserable apathy he was in?

'Don't be stupid! I detest senseless evasions,' Sir Joshua said grandly. 'You're one of us. I know quite well you've got a head on your shoulders. You've had long enough to sum up the situation at Sundown. It belongs to me, you know, for all your great-grandfather built it and lost it!'

'My great-grandfather was a gentleman!' she said loftily, something in his attitude stinging her.

'Who said he wasn't? But gentility, my girl, has nothing to do with being a business man. Some of the biggest rogues I know are gentlemen. All of them had university educations. Not a one of them can hold a candle to me. I built an empire and I started from nothing and nowhere. My grandson is a gentleman, if we must use this silly word of yours, but it doesn't make a man successful!'

'No, of course not. Why are we arguing?' She tried to placate him for no other reason than that he *was* very old, for all the power house of fire and aggression.

'Like all women you can't win an argument, so you want to change the subject. All right, you're in love with Kyle Tyson.'

'Just because I can't get him out of my head or my bloodstream it doesn't mean I'm in love with him!'

'You love him.'

'Is it the kind of love that lasts a lifetime?'

'It's a damn good start. You know you're not the first to say that and you won't be the last. Kyle is the product of a very unhappy home. He is not my son—let me make that clear once and for all and to my deepest regret. I wish to God he was! I'd have done anything, given up every single thing I'd ever ventured out on for Rachael, his mother. But *she* wasn't having any. It was as simple as that. Mark you, she loved me in her own way and I had to be content with that. It was easy for Rachael to tie men to her. Me, her husband, weak as they come and a gentleman, her son. Kyle has the same strong will, that quality of fascination Rachael had. She was different from any woman I've ever known, and I've known a few. Beside Rachael your Aunt Camilla is too frivolous for words, yet she's a clever woman in her fashion, but her life has no meaning. Now you've become a part of it all.'

'I haven't!' protested Gabriele.

'Oh yes, you have. Why do you think you were brought here.'

'My aunt invited me. You can't order my life, Sir Joshua, and I mean no discourtesy!'

'No, you're very polite. Exquisitely so. Kyle wasn't mistaken. I like you. You're true to yourself, but you're very young also. The young usually start me off yawning or put me into a tearing rage. But you're something else again. No, don't withdraw into that cool little shell. Now that I look at you, I can see you'll do Kyle very well!'

'My God, not more machinations!' she said faintly, overwhelmed by the great leaps in the conversation. 'I should die of embarrassment if we were overheard!'

'Oh, don't be foolish,' he said, his brow under his coronet darkening. 'It's about time Kyle married—my only criticism of him. A man is nothing without a son. I should know. You're an intelligent girl. You're young and healthy with the added pleasure of being lovely to look upon. You'll give him a son!'

'*Mon dieu*, what a triumph! This is ridiculous, Sir Joshua, and wishful thinking on both sides. I have no influence whatever on Kyle Tyson!'

'More than you think!' Sir Joshua said slyly. 'Kyle speaks very highly of you. He has, I think, a certain *tendresse* for you. Very unusual for Kyle, if you only knew it. Perhaps it's your youthfulness, the saintliness you're so justly proud of. You know the situation up at the house—inflammable. You know your aunt Camilla is currently obsessed with my godson. She's married to my *grandson*, lest we all forget. Any other set-up or entanglement is out of the question. If so, I'll cut the whole lot of them out of my will. You might as well know I intend to leave Sundown to you.'

Twin lines of bafflement appeared between Gabriele's delicate brows. 'This isn't real, is it? I'm dreaming!'

'While my grandson and his wife remain together, man and wife, the house is theirs!' Sir Joshua said sternly. 'For their lifetime, or until such time as one of them dies. Camilla has a great feel for possessions, property. And she loves the house, let us all rest assured of that even if she doesn't share the same regard for her husband. A lot of the discord between them rests with my grandson. Women like Camilla need a strong hand, but there's not a bit of use her hankering after my godson. Oh no, that I will not allow, and I always succeed in my manoeuvres. You will do very much better. Should Paul and Camilla go their separate ways or, as I say, either one of them dies, the estate passes to you intact, to your children. My godson's, God willing. I'd like that. You're Old Lawrence's granddaughter. I liked him. He was a fine old chap in lots of ways, but he wasn't cunning or ruthless enough. One must be that—regrettable but true!'

'And this is how I came into all this?' she asked, her voice elaborately quiet, the blood running to her cheeks.

'You don't really think your aunt sent for you?' Sir Joshua asked with weary impatience. 'So far as your aunt was concerned you might never have seen Sundown. It was Kyle who wanted you here. Why should that child be all alone? was all he said. After that, it was easy. Things fell into place as they always do for me. I knew from the photograph up at the house that you couldn't be ugly. Such a beautiful child could only become a beautiful woman. You constitute a new element. It rather pleases me to score off Camilla and with her own niece. I don't like what she's doing!'

'And I don't like what you're doing, Sir Joshua!' she said with some irony. 'I won't be a part of it. You strike me as a bit of a *malicieux!*'

Instead of being insulted, he just laughed. 'Tell me something I don't know! You're caught up in this, child, as surely as the rest of us. I tell you, you can get Kyle to marry you with only a little feminine guile. He's very much like Rachael under it all. He has a great sense of what's suitable. And you are suitable, unquestionably a lady, to use your own damned fool terminology. As much as he dislikes the idea, Kyle knows he must marry some time. He is my successor, there's no going back on that. I would be doing myself and my hundreds of employees a disservice if I nominated anyone else. Paul, even if he did take a more active interest in the Organisation, simply hasn't got the business sense. Tycoons are born, not made, like great pianists. What do you say, child?'

'I don't share your talent for intrigue, Sir Joshua. If it's my good fortune or misfortune to love Kyle Tyson I won't lift a finger to bind him to me and I won't be a party to anything that smacks of intrigue. I don't like it!'

'Oh, grow up, girlie,' he said, trying not to smile. 'You can't play the ingénue for ever. Marriages aren't made in heaven, for all the rubbish you've stuffed your head with!'

'So why are you telling me all this?'

'Because I'm an old man,' he said calmly, 'and I've had it!'

'You look pretty remarkable to me!'

'Well, I'm not!' he said rather ill-temperedly. 'Not any more. I don't feel the same. Another fall will see me out. I don't want to live much longer in any case.

I've had my day, and what a day it was! The only thing of value I missed out on was Rachael. The one and only time she told me she loved me was when she was dying. Imagine that! But I knew, and so did that fool husband of hers. An empty gesture in lots of ways, Rachael trying to preserve her marriage, pulling the boy two ways. He adored his mother and it was bad for him. Nothing was the same after we met! Yet Tyson wasn't a bad chap. Old school tie and all that, straight as they come, but not the man for Rachael. She was by far the dominant personality. Not good for a woman to dominate. A true woman revels in admiring her man. She wants to respect him as her companion and protector, her lover. No, my dear, I repent nothing. If I had my life over again I'd do the same things, only this time I'd have Rachael and Kyle would be my son!'

Even for an old man there was a passionate wistfulness about his expression, and Gabriele, touched, reached out for his hand. 'Don't let's talk any more about it, Sir Joshua. The earth is always beautiful—the bluer than blue sky, the green silence. Tell me about the vines. I understand you're an authority!'

'And you keep your head splendidly. Come, child, I suppose you know our wines here on Sundown have a strong bouquet of cedar. Well, do you know why?'

Sir Joshua had arrived. Not a man, woman or child on the estate didn't know it, making the holiday atmosphere anything but festive. Sir Joshua was a born 'stirrer', unable to spend a single day in the backwaters of placidity. Life for Sir Joshua had been full of tempest and storm, a state of affairs he had come to enjoy and expect, making it very natural for him to rock everyone else's boat mercilessly. From early morning to late at

141

night, and he kept long hours, he teased the children, alternately petted and shouted at the household pets, heckled his grandson who steadfastly refused to rise to the bait, and took a malicious pleasure in pointing out to his hostess some trifling defect in the running of Sundown as though it was tantamount to ruin. *His*. Camilla, though she was inwardly rigid with hate and resentment, was as good in her fashion as Sir Joshua was in his, for she never allowed him to ruffle her magnificent calm. And he tried very hard.

Gabriele when she had called him a *malicieux* had not been very far from the truth. Sir Joshua actually liked antagonising people, or in his own words 'getting them going!' To Gabriele, who saw little to be gained in condoning his active bursts of aggression, he was very cordial indeed. Not completely because he liked her, which he did, but rather it irritated Camilla, who was the hidden target for most of his attacks and an opponent worthy of his salt. All would have been well with the cold war continuing right over the Christmas, only for the reappearance of Kyle Tyson, Camilla's house guest for the holiday period.

After that the atmosphere worsened to cyclonic, as explosive as chain lightning, as though Sir Joshua was bent on forcing out into the open the subversive element in the house. Gabriele, a lover of peace, loathed the whole set-up, only hoped she would be spared a major scene on her birthday. A troublemaker Sir Joshua might be, but he was anything but dull, very quick-witted and funny, but an 'old devil', she was forced to admit, even if she had arrived at a fondness for him. Sir Joshua was far too remarkable a human being to earn indifference and she fancied she saw in him much of the *enfant terrible*, excessively high-spirited, and a natural hazard for everybody around. This tempered her attitude to-wards him so much so that all unaware Sir Joshua had enlisted her into his camp should the house break up into two factions.

Camilla too was bent on precipitating a climax of her own, but on her own terms and in her own time. She detested being stage-managed. A beautiful woman fast approaching forty, she was entering a tremendously difficult period in her life when she could only expect her powers to wane. Another seven years at the outside was what she gave herself. Up until the present she had maintained her stunning good looks almost unimpaired, but her day would come. No woman on earth could stave it off. At these dreadful moments of truth in front of her mirror Camilla momentarily raged against life, cruel to a great beauty. One could almost wish one had been born plain. The next seven years, she resolved, she would take and live to the utmost before her inevitable decline was forced on her. She would never accept it gladly.

Then too, like everyone else, she decided she had missed the boat. Paul was a fool and a 'cake'. She had had enough of him. No man in her life had so excited her as Kyle Tyson, and he was playing phenomenally hard to get, which only made the whole thing that much more shattering. All of them, with the exception of Sir Joshua, were civilised human beings. They would settle their affairs accordingly. There was little point in living out a stale marriage. Of course she would have the children. She adored them and they were ready for boarding school.

Of her niece Gabriele, all white and golden, and increasingly eye-catching of late, she had grown deeply apprehensive. A threat on her very doorstep. A viper in her bosom and, could she bring herself to admit it, stiff competition. One's life was over scarcely before it had begun. She had never really begun to enjoy herself until she had met Kyle. Her marriage to Paul had been traditional, a planned assault right down to the last detail, a society coup. She could never, never have borne to marry a poor man. Of the two, she would much rather settle for money than love. Not like Paula, who had married her Drew and be damned to her. Of Drew Somerville Camilla never allowed herself to think at all. He was one of her few failures, though she had only been trying to fascinate him, after all. Struggling young architects had never been her scene.

Always supremely confident of her powers of sexual attraction, Camilla was now for the first time in her life assailed by niggling doubts, the anxiety occasioned by not being certain of being able to get what one wanted. It didn't make her kind or tolerant. But on Sir Joshua's instructions she went about organising a gala birthday-cum-Christmas party for her niece, who had somehow become Sir Joshua's darling. The sooner the girl was packed and away the better, Camilla reasoned, but how she was going to organise that called for some masterly thinking. Sir Joshua was dead set on Gabriele's remaining at Sundown, and Sir Joshua footed the bills. One had to handle the old demon with kid gloves or else one became singed. Still, he couldn't last for ever and this gave Camilla comfort. One day soon she would have what she really hungered for—love and a lot of money. One wasn't much good without the other.

And so it was left to Gabriele and the children to decorate the tree, stately and beautiful. Hang the tapering branches with innumerable expensive baubles, jewel-coloured ornaments, streamers of tinsel, silver and gold dust and fibre-glass 'snow'. Beneath it sat the gaily papered, professionally gift-wrapped boxes Aunt Camilla said they might put under the tree. To the back of these, tucked under a tinkling ornament, Gabriele and the children put their own modest contributions, carefully considered then purchased on a joint shopping expedition, for all three if no one else in the house were on a pretty tight budget.

While they worked Gabriele felt the sting of salt tears in her eyes. This was her first birthday, her first Christmas without her beloved parents, and she was sad at heart. Impossible not to feel that way, and equally impossible to show it and upset the children. She loved them and she was certain they loved her, so they sang all the carols they could think of, Melissa recited, Paul whistled very pleasingly through his teeth and all the tree needed was the Christmas angel reserved for the top.

'A least Mamma will be home *this* time!' Melissa said appealingly. 'Last Christmas Eve she went out to the Whitneys'. Ugh! I hate them and their terrible child. Daddy said he was more considerate and stayed home!' A look of the deepest longing crossed her face. 'Oh, I'll be glad when I'm twenty. I can't wait to grow up. I'm going to cause a sensation!'

'I'll bet you are!' Paul retorted, more concerned than impressed.

'Oh, I say, watch yourself, Gabby, you'll fall off,' Melissa cautioned. 'The rope's not pulled out far enough!' Urgently she began tugging at the flared cuff of Gabriele's slacks. 'Have a care! I can't watch. I'm going to shut my eyes!'

'You're going to pull her off, you mean! Let go, silly!' Paul reached over and tapped his sister sharply on the elbow with a full roll of wrapping paper. In a reflex action Melissa grabbed at the stepladder and it jerked violently. Precariously perched, as Melissa had so acutely pointed out, Gabriele was flung out sideways, her hand behind her to break her fall.

The crack of her head against the brass inlaid cabinet was audible, drawing forth Melissa's sincerely melodramatic:

'Speak to me! God, she's not dead?'

'Are you *crazy*?' Paul asked vehemently, shuddering, his animated little face gone white. 'It just shows what comes of letting *you* help us!' he burst out man-fashion.

'I'm sorry!' sniffed Melissa.

'What's the use of being sorry? The harm's done.'

'In another minute you'll begin prayers over me and start showering lilies!' Gabriele put up a hand to her instantly throbbing head. The blow had been like an explosion of light, quite literally. 'A lovely thing to happen on my birthday!'

'Oh God!' Melissa bent and kissed her fiercely, and painfully too, as it happened. 'I'm so sorry. It's all my fault. Just as well it wasn't a proper ladder, otherwise, who knows, you might never have seen another birthday. Think of that!'

'Oh, shut up!' her brother said, projecting into his voice a whole world of impatience. 'I think you're pretty well off your head, and you're only eight. You'll be a sensation all right! Do you think you can get up, old girl?' he so addressed Gabriele, who couldn't help smiling as much at the 'old girl' as anything else. She was double his age, after all.

'It will be a few more moments before I condescend to do so!' she said. 'I seem to be jarred right down to my toes.'

'You're lucky at that!' Melissa swivelled her head. 'Another few inches or if your legs were a bit longer you'd have knocked that blanc de Chine Buddha off its stand. She's lovely, isn't she, the Kuan Yin? You'd probably have hundreds of years of bad luck, not to speak of Mamma's enmity for life!'

'She really is crazy!' Paul said softly by way of explanation.

'It looks like it. Doesn't it?'

'That's right, go on. Comfort my pride!' Melissa burst out.

'What the devil does *that* mean?'

So engrossed were they as a trio, the one on the ground, that a tall figure was upon them before the children broke off their argument.

'What in the world goes on?' Kyle dropped to his knees beside Gabriele, a frown between his dark brows. Never having much colour, she was paper white. 'Gabriel?' Gently he turned her face from side to side.

'I did it. It was I!' Melissa informed him like a grammatical martyr, determined not to be done out of a punishment. 'I wiggled the ladder and Gabby came off. Just like that!'

'She hit her head there on the cabinet,' Paul supplied, pointing to the long hairs caught around a brass hinge.

'I think she's hysterical!' Melissa said thoughtfully.

'I think you're wanted urgently some place else,' Paul hissed at her.

'Both of you, actually!' Kyle said evenly, his fingers finding the swelling at the base of Gabriele's skull.

'Why didn't you tell us?' Melissa gave a movement of surprise. 'We can't leave the patient in any case!'

'The skin isn't broken!' Kyle said consolingly.

'Saints be praised!'

'It's all right, I'll take her away, Uncle Kyle.' Paul grabbed his voluble little sister's hand. 'Will you be all right, Gabby?'

'I'll look after her!' Kyle said briefly, turning his dark head. 'The tree looks lovely anyway!'

'Oh, thank you, Uncle Kyle!' Melissa said happily, responding to praise. 'I guess some mysterious power brought you here, right at this minute. I love your shirt and tie! The little dots match.'

'Run along, sweetheart,' he said easily. 'The patient must have some air, and you seem to be taking up most of it!'

'Right-oh. Shall we tell anyone?'

'No!'

Then they were alone. 'If that child would only grow up, I think I'd marry her,' Kyle said lightly, a silver shimmer of amusement in his eyes. 'You're not dizzy, are you?'

'A little. It hurts a lot.'

'Not surprising. There's no padding between the skin and the bone. Happy birthday, Gabriele!' He bent over her and brushed her mouth with his own. 'This seems to be the only way I can get to talk to you these days. No, don't move for a moment. I like it here. You look better already!'

'Why wouldn't I? I like kisses for my birthday. Forget the falls!'

'Is this Gabriele?' he smiled at her. 'So provocative and such a snow maiden of late. If your head was only better we could discuss your engagement. Surely you've drawn a list up of presents and so forth. Kill two birds with the one stone. Am I to offer my best wishes, or is it to be announced tonight?'

Just to have him there, so handsome and mocking, so

impossibly intent on her was a gift beyond all price. The silver gaze travelled over her, the long lean body relaxed yet alert, very elegant in its city clothes. He could do with a jolt if a jolt it was.

'Oh, tonight, when else?' she said flippantly. She took a deep breath, but there just wasn't time. There was a flash in his eyes that completely dispelled the illusion of lazy admiration. One lean hand slid over the delicate curve of her shoulder and he kissed her a second time, in a stunningly adult, very devastating fashion.

'If you don't stop I'll faint!' she protested very faintly against his mouth, every nerve in her body tingling, leaping into chaotic response. Another minute and she would forget her own identity.

'One must take one's kisses when one can!' he said grimly, and lifted his head. 'Especially with you. Announce any engagement to that idiot Danton and I'll undertake to strangle you myself. With your own hair!'

He didn't meet her smoky gaze directly but pushed the smooth shining hair off her shoulder. 'Now, belatedly, what about a couple of aspirins or whatever else you take?'

'Having shaken me up properly, that's quite a good suggestion. Why do you do it?'

'What?' In one lithe movement he was on his feet again, then turned to lift her gently to her feet, holding her steady, his hands slipping from her shoulders to her narrow waist.

'Oh, forget it!' she said recklessly. 'The city's awash with your conquests!'

'And you're going to survive to regret *that* one. But for now, we must remember your head. How is it, anyway?'

She arched her neck back experimentally and shut her

eyes considering. 'Surprisingly, not too bad at all!'

'Good!'

Something else again in that dry tone made her eyes fly open again, wide and startled, dove-soft. His silvery, lancing gaze was full on her face, so charged with a kind of sexual radiance that she was shaken.

'Don't dither!' he said, gently sardonic. 'What are *you* trying to do, if it comes to that?'

'How should *I* know?' she sighed audibly. 'I've no confidence whatever when you're around.'

'Now why say that? You're the fastest learner I've ever encountered. In fact, Gabriele, you're a man's dream of what a woman should be. A marrying man, that is!'

'You shouldn't say things like that if you don't mean them!' her low voice reproved him.

'Who said I don't mean it? I thought you'd appreciate a frank answer. Can I be blamed if I'm feeling the pull of your fascination in spite of my convictions!'

His eyes were gleaming, brilliantly mocking, the flash of the sun on winter ice, and Gabriele made a little wry face at him. 'Don't worry, I'll soon have your measure, Kyle Tyson.'

'That's what I'm afraid of!' His voice, dark and sardonic, slowed to a drawl. 'Now come along, little one. I've a present for you lest you fall into the sulks on your own.'

She expelled a long breath and looked up into his face, so fantastically alive. He really did make her feel faint.

'You must have been a dreadful little boy!'

There was a faint cynical line to his mouth. 'So my mother always said. Don't you want to know what it is?'

'All things come to her who waits, is my motto.'

'Is it really, Gabriele?' With a kind of coiled alertness

he put out a hand and lifted her face. 'Say that again!'

'No. You're too good at this sort of thing!' The words were drawn from her, very serious and soft.

'And you're improving all the time. Don't give up now!' He seemed to relent, for he smiled at her, that white attractive smile. 'I'm sorry, Gabriele, I keep forgetting your head. You simply grow too lovely, and that's the sad fact. Now, if I were you, I wouldn't bother coming down again!' he said, crisply decisive, the man in command again. 'Just take it easy until tonight when I'm sure you'll dazzle us all. Have a tray in your room. I'll look after the kids for the rest of the afternoon. I've finished all I have to do.'

'You're so good ... so *sweet* to me,' she found herself saying satirically. 'I don't think anyone else quite realises!'

'Really?' His voice had an odd note to it that whipped her back to reality. She looked about her a little uncertainly, then took to her heels, sparks flying around her feet, every inch of her burning! What an implacable set he could get to his head. Its arrogant dark image possessed her all the way up the stairs and it was still there when she collapsed on the bed. She would never, *never* be certain of him, but this giddy uncertain excitement was better by far than the knowledge that it was only a game. A good student, were she to sit for an exam this very day she would only be able to write *Kyle* all over the pages. So much for equality between the sexes. At a board meeting he would be hard pressed to remember her name.

CHAPTER EIGHT

SIR JOSHUA stayed twenty minutes at the party, no more.

'And no present for you either!' he told Gabriele firmly the moment he saw her. 'I've told you what you're getting and a bit more. A small income. You'll be independent. No sense in ruining you altogether. You look lovely too, my dear,' he added a bit gruffly, not missing the slightest detail of her appearance. 'Very young and innocent. Irresistible to most men, should you have any doubts. Remember what I told you,' he added, in a cautious aside.

'I'm trying to forget, Sir Joshua!'

'That's likely! Do you think I'm a fool, girl?'

'Never that. I just hope there aren't many people here tonight with your perceptions!'

'And no worries about that!' Sir Joshua retorted with some asperity. 'All they live for is parties. No, my dear, only the common clay of humanity are here tonight. They ought to put that silly Danton woman on a boat and send her around the world—anything to get her out of Kyle's hair. Distinguished Official Hostess or something equally ridiculous. Women grow sillier if anything. Desperate, some of them. Now, I'm off before she tries to waylay me. Send Kyle to me, like a good girl. I'm devlish tired of late. I'd fly into a mad rage if I were twenty years younger, and any younger than that, you and I would take the town by the ears. It only struck me the other night you have a little of what Rachael had, some mysterious pull. The siren song, yet very elusive. Invisible chains, I call 'em!'

'Not chains, surely, Sir Joshua?'

'Yes, chains, my dear,' he said soberly. 'I've never lost them. Some women have the power to move and influence men, mostly against their better judgment. Ah, here's Kyle now coming across to us. Camilla hasn't let him out of her sight, you'll notice—and just look at that damned fool grandson of mine hovering just outside the magic circle. It's a wonder he doesn't hide from all eyes. Yet he's an imposing-looking creature, wouldn't you say? Yes, you would, for you always defend him. I'd like to get after him with a stick of dynamite. I will too, given the opportunity!'

Lightly Gabriele took his arm, feeling the anger in him. 'Perhaps it's just as well you're going up to bed, then! Don't worry, Sir Joshua, everything will work out.'

'I don't think so!' he shrugged his still straight shoulders. 'And I'm a lot wiser than you. Ah, good evening, my boy! A word or two before I retire. Gabriele here is such a chatterbox she'd have me up all night!'

Kyle was beside them, his light eyes flicking Gabriele's face and bare shoulders. 'Won't I do as a substitute, little one?'

'If you weren't such a damned hard worker, I'd say you were a determined philanderer!' Sir Joshua remarked slyly, his pride and affection implicit in his eyes.

'So I understand,' Kyle murmured laconically. 'Twice in one night. Gabriele has said very much the same thing to me.'

'Well, knock me down with a feather,' Sir Joshua returned. 'What an ungrateful child! I didn't miss the earrings and I couldn't look too long at the necklace for fear of getting a bad name. Why don't you settle that libel once and for all, my boy? Get married!'

'What do *you* think, Gabriele?' Kyle turned to her with the challenge.

'I have no views on the matter!' she said, and evaded Sir Joshua's shrewd, clever eyes.

Sir Joshua exploded into laughter that caused several heads to turn towards them. 'She'd never have said such a thing to me. That was a little cruel, wasn't it, my dear?'

'You won't catch me out, Sir Joshua. I'm going. Good night, and sleep well!' Gabriele moved a little nearer in her swirling chiffon gown, tipping up her face to kiss the cheek so confidently presented to her.

'You're a credit to your parents. To your sex and to yourself!' Sir Joshua said with no trace of pleasant indulgence, very serious all of a sudden, a slight tremor in his rather harsh voice.

'Thank you, Sir Joshua!' she said impulsively, taking his hand. 'I'll always remember that, and your great kindness to me!'

'Don't go too far away!' Kyle said over his shoulder, and began to steer Sir Joshua through the crowd that soon parted with almost mechanical precision. The old man was weary and he didn't care who knew it. Camilla came at a rush and Kyle held up his hand to still her flight, but he made no such movement when Paul Lynnton joined them at the other side of the old man. The three of them, moving now in perfect accord, had trapped the attention of every single person in that room—the last time any of them would see Sir Joshua again. A funny little shiver of premonition ran down Gabriele's nape. Impulsively she wanted to run after them, but couldn't think exactly why. Then the little tableau broke and Camilla came across to her, doe eyes glittering all over the picture her niece made, fair as a dream.

'Dearest, you'll really have to circulate a bit more. There's no use trying to capture Sir Joshua's attention. Quite impossible. Thank God he's gone off to bed. I had the very dismal notion he might try to provoke a scene. He cares nothing whatever for the conventions, as I expect you know!' All the while she was talking Camilla's enormous black eyes were focused on Gabriele's delicate pendant necklace and matching pendant earrings, translucent pearls and enamels set in gold, much more valuable than Gabriele would ever have supposed, not being familiar with authentic antique jewellery. Camilla *was*, and colour whipped into her face, making her stunningly beautiful, a tigress in her dull bronze gown that superbly complemented her dark magnificence. 'Where did you get that?' she asked quite conversationally.

If only it were a charm to protect her, Gabriele thought her hand straying to her new, prize possession. 'A birthday preasent,' she said, equally pleasant.

'Don't be dreary, dearest, from *whom?*'

'It was Kyle, I think!' said Gabriele, cursing her own cowardice, or rather her deep-seated aversion to scenes.

'Beware the Greeks!' Camilla trilled at her. 'My poor little girl, I think you and I will have to have a talk. Facts of life and all that!' She had a high, brilliant colour, a set look as though she was making a physical effort not to say too much.

'I know enough, I hope!' Gabriele said gravely, and Camilla gave another bell peal of laughter.

'Things are a lot trickier than at first they seem. But never mind, dearest, I remember quite well what it was like at your age. Happy birthday!' And then she was gone, with her quick, lovely movements.

If I had her present in my hand right now I bet it would explode! Gabriele thought wryly. All of a sudden on Christmas Eve, on her birthday, she was unbearably saddened. Her mood that had fluctuated all the day seemed to have settled. She was so very receptive to atmosphere. Sir Joshua, Kyle, Paul's lack of decision, beautiful Aunt Camilla, so like and so unlike her own mother, the brittle gaiety that masked heaven knew what. It would be hell to love with no hope of return. She wasn't long alone with her reflections, for Noel came to claim her like some victorious knight, for once very slightly drunk.

'Angel, you're a work of genius tonight!' His hazel eyes devoured her. 'I don't go much for the old jewellery. Your mother's? I like the modern stuff! Or gorgeous chunks of rock like Camilla's. But the dress and your hair set me a-trembling. They say the Old Man's here tonight. Where is he?'

'Gone up to bed. He looked very tired and white!'

'Oh, he'll live to fight another day, don't worry about that. And the Crown Prince?'

'Uncle Paul's gone up with him!' she said, disproportionately angry.

'S'truth, love, don't be obtuse!' Noel answered cheerfully enough, unaware of her anger. 'Old Paul has gotten himself so much in a rut, he'll never get out. It's Tyson I'm talking about. I presumed, among other things, you'd know *that!*'

She never forgave him. 'It's my birthday!' she said oddly, looking over his blond head at Camilla's wild dark beauty.

'Well!' Noel said with the liveliest surprise. 'Why ever have you kept it a secret? This calls for champagne.

I'll call for you the very first day the shops open and we'll take the whole day to decide which one you want!'

'Which one what?' she asked, unable to endure it.

But Noel wouldn't put a name to it; his smile persisted, knowing, very persuasive in the heady state he was in. Tonight, her hair was pulled back but falling loose in the way he liked. Her slender young body was half turned away from him, so full of unconscious allure. The smoky drift of chiffon was almost the colour of her eyes. It dawned on him as he stared at her that the old-fashioned jewellery exactly suited her. How odd! She attracted him madly, yet she wasn't his style, and it was unsettling, exciting. Her wide, black-lashed eyes looked faintly haunted, and this too he found disturbing, visualising her quite still and utterly acquiescent in his arms. It was quite possible she was cold, and a frown knotted his brow. Tonight he would find out. Kiss 'em senseless was an infallible method and one he had found very hard to put into practice. It required a certain panache, a confidence he was lacking. But there was always the champagne. Only a social drinker, he was entitled to this one night and he was feeling very successful. One couldn't allow the stimulus to run out. 'I'll just collect the bubbly and a couple of glasses,' he explained. 'None of your lemon squash tonight!'

Gabriele sat down for a moment feeling utterly amazed, remote in her lack of gaiety or even well-being. Perhaps it was the crack on the head, but she felt a bundle of nerves, sad and apprehensive. Across the room she could see Noel arrested and detained by a very grand-looking woman in bottle green, and she breathed an audible sigh of relief. Had she really expected to feel less than forlorn on this first anniversary? Tears stung her eyes again and she moved swiftly, holding her eyes wide, her skirt floating behind her in a silver wake.

'Oh, Gabby!'

It was Aunt Camilla's voice that halted her, sweet as run honey, but imperious.

'Yes?' Gabriele turned quickly to look into those enormous doe eyes with their little shooting sparks.

'A favour, dearest, and everyone else seems to be occupied. Slip down to the cellar and bring up another half-dozen Pol Roget. Leave them in the kitchen—Marie will ice them. I expect she's flat out at the moment. We may need them later on. It's such a hot evening!'

Gabriele moved away as graceful as a gazelle and Camilla called after her, 'Mind the door. Leave it open— it's inclined to bang shut!'

The cellar was a spooky old place, haunted, and if Gabriele had not been a grown woman she would have refused point blank to have gone down. The bottles were stacked with meticulous care, row upon row in cool corridors, lying on their sides in geometric perfection to keep their corks moist. It was airless down there, or seemed to be. It reminded her vaguely of the caves she had visited once on holiday, tourist attractions, but not for her or her mother. Neither of them had been able to venture more than a few feet into the low-vaulted, airless interior, being seized by sensations far more primitive than a simple claustrophobia. Shortlived as that experience had been it had proved traumatic. Even this cellar bothered her, so cool and dim, lit by only one unshaded electric light bulb, for ever denied the sunlight, for sunlight was disastrous for the storing of wines.

Gabriele looked along the lines. Sherries and dessert wines. Cocktails, Vermouth, table wines, the dry reds and the whites, the sweet white and rosés. It was sparkling wine she wanted. Not domestic either but the unexcelled French champagne, Pol Roget, Aunt Camilla had said. It was all a little confusing. Why hadn't Aunt Camilla come herself? She knew exactly where every last bottle was kept and it was extremely unlike her to underestimate the evening's requirements. If anything there was always an excess at Sundown.

How cold it was down here. And dusty! Aunt Camilla would have known that. Yet the bottles were beautiful when held up to the light. Jewel colours, all the reds, ruby and amethyst, but the reds gripped her palate with the tannin finish. She wasn't ready for them yet.

With a sickening lurch, her senses alerted almost before the incident; she heard the massive cedar door swing shut. It plodded heavily into place and remained rock firm like an entity to block her way to the light and fresh air. The silence seemed to intensify and smother her, draining away all her vitality in an instant. It was the cave again—but she had to rationalise her fear. And fear it was, not panic. Not a chink of light showed above or below the old door's studded proportions.

Activity would drive out this fear. Gabriele swallowed hard on a rising lump in her throat and picked up her filmy skirts to remount the steep flight of steps. A marked shiver swept her whole body. What a fool thing to happen—and Aunt Camilla *had* warned her. She hadn't been careful enough, though the old door had seemed secure, wide open. There were no draughts. None of the household staff, knowing the door's idosyncrasies, would have closed it without first checking downstairs. She could possibly open it from this side with her small, slender fingers—the nails perhaps. No, she tried this in vain, then took off her evening sandal and thumped on the door, then again, much louder this time, with no thought of her fragile sandal; her predicament seemed to warrant it. One would have thought she was alone, deserted, instead of in a house full of people. Had she been cast into darkness as well, she would undoubtedly have screamed and shamed herself for ever.

She stood quite still for a moment before the old cedar monolith, trying to control her shaking nerves. Someone would come. Aunt Camilla would miss her. All she had to do was wait and not let her fear of confined spaces get the better of her. It would be an exercise in will power. Someone would come. Though with Sir Joshua gone to bed she was no longer the guest of honour. Her birthday it might be, but it was Camilla's party. Let no one forget.

Gabriele walked quietly, very subdued, down the steps. She would put her mind to finding the half-dozen bottles and by the time she had found them Aunt Camilla would be there at the top of the stairs, her sweet voice urging her to hurry up! There was no need for her to walk so quietly as if the cellar was crammed full of ghosts. Why didn't she behave like a solid, sensible ordinary person? —yet even ordinary people were conditioned to receiving odd sensations in certain places. The old wine cellar wasn't a cemetery, for instance, yet she would much rather have been in a cemetery. It was the feeling of being shut in that was producing these sick moments.

Half an hour went by and no one came. The quiet beat about her with muffled wings. There was an occasional rustle back there in the shadows—mice. Gabriele crossed her arms about her, a little unnerved. She would probably remember this evening for the rest of her life, yet it wasn't so bad really. Locked in a wine cellar. If she were a drinker she would have no cause for complaint. She could start in on any of those silver and gold-capped bottles. Or some of the spirits perhaps—Scotch whisky.

Her father used to like that, but it had the same appeal for her as castor oil. Preposterous to think Aunt Camilla could have forgotten her. Yet why not? Hours passed like minutes at parties, especially when one was the brilliant centre of attention.

Gabriele smiled a little, trying to cheer herself up, but felt no less frightened. She was lonely, unbearably lonely. There were cobwebs that clung to the walls and the ceilings—spiders, probably. Someone would come. She clung to it with a blind faith. She only wished they would hurry. She seemed to be having trouble swallowing. The sore spot at the base of her skull had started up throbbing again. She bent her head, waiting. It was hard to know what else to do. She could make no impression whatever on that door. It was a very effective trap, the wine cellar.

The brilliant lights from the chandeliers, the party, the sparkling Christmas tree, the flashing colours of the dresses and the flowers, all seemed a far-off dream. *Kyle!* Where was he? Don't go too far away, he had said. Gabriele touched the softly glowing pendant that swung to her breast. It hadn't protected her at all. When they finally opened the door she would be a shadow of herself—crazy, most probably. Today seemed to have carried more than its fair freight of nervous reaction.

'At the raising of Lazarus someone said,
what was it like, in the dark with the dead?'

She spoke the words aloud with every appearance of lightness, but they were best not recited in the depths of the cellar. She tried for self-protection to see the funny side, but for once her sense of humour failed her. She sat in her old wooden chair like a throne. What if the roof fell in on her? The roof of the cave. She drew in her breath, softly, almost guardedly, not recognising that her inner tensions were drawing to breaking point.

Light seemed to flare from the top of the stairs in a silver sword flash, an aurora for a tall, dark frame. Gabriele was helpless. She couldn't get up and he seemed to know it. Then she was lying against him, the living warmth and the strength of him. His dark head was bent over her own and she could feel the steady thud of his heart, an exchange of vitality that was bringing life back into her limbs. He was holding her in complete silence; neither of them had said a word. Words didn't seem necessary. His dark face had tautened as if under pressure, his narrowed eyes mere silver chips, but she didn't see that! Her own face was buried in the soft ruffles of his shirt, her shoulder curving to the palm of his hand.

Her delicate face was extremely pale, her grey eyes closed, her heavy lashes sweeping her cheeks, instinctively taking in full measure the comfort that was so soundlessly offered. She made a funny litttle sound of recent distress and his hard, handsome face softened to compassion.

'That was a clever trick, locking yourself in the cellar!' he said gently. 'No one else seems to have been able to do that, without a little outside help! And you're so helpless, Gabriele. Taking comfort like an eight-year-old when I know you're a woman. I can feel your heart race. Look at me!'

Something in that smooth, low tone filled her with flame, so wild and so warming it was instant vitality. She turned up her head and her wide smoky eyes swept his face, the pupils dilated, irises intensely illuminated. He mouth, a deep frosted pink, was softly pulsing, sensitive and sensuous, her skin in the glare from the unshaded light exquisitely young.

'Consider very carefully that you've given me a few

bad moments!' he said very dryly. 'About ten in all since I came downstairs. Sir Joshua was rather hard to settle. I was worried enough about him, then *you*. You seem to invite trouble, Gabriele!'

Her head was tilted back over his arm, her hair a silver-gilt stream over the black cloth of his evening jacket. 'You can't imagine what it was like down here. I'm no good at all at that kind of thing!' Remembrance made her shaky and she moistened her mouth with the tip of her tongue.

'I know!' he said rather tautly. 'And it might pay to get moving now. It's costing me an effort to keep treating you like a baby girl child when you're really a witch, for all the silvery curls!'

'I'm sorry!' She tried to pull away, a little breathless, realising with a pang how her reserve had melted away.

His hand and his voice were calming, casual even. 'Stay there. You're entitled to a few moments. I might even let you cry all over my shirt. It's brand new, too!'

'There's no need for that,' she said swiftly, her voice not much more than a grateful whisper. 'You've no idea how I wanted you here. *Prayed* for you!'

'Oh God!' The exclamation was completely devoid of reverence or amusement. Kyle stretched out his hand and ran a finger down her cheek, but instead of easing her tensions they were mounting. The lean fingers brushed her throat and she shivered. 'I love my necklace and earrings,' she said with charming intensity. 'I haven't had the opportunity to tell you before this!'

'You told Camilla!' he said briefly, his eyes on the fresh pearl at her breast.

'She asked me!' she explained quickly—he looked so forbiddingly handsome. 'It wasn't deliberate.'

'Deliberate, in what way?'

'I knew it would annoy her!' was all she could manage, desperate to change the subject.

'She's jealous!' he supplied.

'Of me?'

'Why not? She knows I want to make love to you every time I see you—like now. But you're just a child, still doing your lessons. Too young!'

'I'm not! Can't you believe me?'

'I don't want to, Gabriele!'

A cool indifference seemed to prowl in his light eyes and it fired her pride. '*I'm* afraid of the wine cellar, and *you're* afraid of women!'

'Not women, Gabriele. You!'

A dynamic intensity was reflected in his face, a kind of rejection, but her eyes were a woman's weapon to be drawn on at will.

'Kiss me!' she said softly. 'It's my birthday, I've had several nasty experiences and I want you to, so badly!'

His strange eyes glittered all over her face. 'What about your fiancé?'

It was agony, a humiliation, that laugh in his voice. The slightest, disconcerting catch. Gabriele closed her small fist and hit him on a wave of frustration, an easy, mocking target. 'You torment!' she said wildly. 'You wicked tease and torment!'

Then she was locked in his arms, her two wrists pinned, and her head tilted on its slender neck. The light bulb seemed to swing crazily as he lowered his head, clear and sharp against the weird light. She was all set to resist him, to re-establish her own ego, but she found she simply wasn't able. Pride was a will-o'-the-wisp and Kyle was all about her. The strength and the arrogance, the authority of his touch, the clean, male scent of him, his mouth hard and searching, *punishing*, yet his hands caressed the nape of her neck. She murmured his name on a little surge of defeat and the anger, antagonism whatever it was, seemed to go out of him. Only the sweetness remained, an onrush of excitement that was blinding, mounting in rhythm. He must know how she felt. Starving ... she could never get used to him. With a convulsive movement she arched nearer him and he broke her hold with stunning swiftness, punishing her for her temerity.

'I won't even attempt a defence,' he said with some irony. 'There's none anyway. I even seem to have forgotten the rules for survival. And I'm going to hold you to blame, Gabriele. You have a response to a man that's little short of miraculous!'

'Not *a* man. *You!*' she announced with some passion. 'But I'll tell you right now, Kyle Tyson, I don't *like* you. Not one little bit.'

'Incongruous to admit it, so leave it for now!' A brittle little smile, was it insolence? played about his mouth. 'There's such a thing as showing a little gratitude, Gabriele, not to speak of tact. After all, I did rescue you. Danton is still combing the grounds with the dogs at his heels.'

His eyes were a silvery dazzle of mockery and she shied away from that mockery as if it were poisoned darts. 'Besides,' he said lightly, 'I find it very difficult not to like you. Especially that unexpected little spurt of temper. Who wants a sugar angel? Now, before the situation deteriorates altogether, I'd better take charge. I'm the only adult here!' Carelessly he brought them both to their feet and steadied her, though she soon slipped away from him. 'Let's go back to the party, if that's what it is. I'm not sure if it's the best or the worst you bring out in me!'

'The worst!' she confirmed instantly, and he turned and kissed her mouth hard.

'So *there!* The one thing I won't tolerate from you, Gabriele, is a lot of backchat. I come in handy at times, you're forced to admit.'

She was a cool figurine no longer, breathing rapidly, colour under her skin, trying to impose composure on her leaping pulses. 'I was down here for something!' she said pathetically.

'Forget it!' he said, very abruptly indeed.

'Six bottles of Pol Roget!' she continued distractedly as if he hadn't spoken.

'You were down here, my lamb,' he pointed out testily, 'to be out of the way for half an hour or so. Wake up, little one, and observe things about you. These days you can't trust your own aunty!'

'You can't mean that!' she said. There was something unbearably cynical about his tone, amused and rather ruthless.

'I do. Do you wonder I go in fear of your fair sex!'

'Yet you continue to treat them in exactly the same way.'

'Oh, how's that?' One winged black brow shot up.

'You *know!*' she said with an agitated little flicker of her head that brought silvery tendrils onto her cheeks and her brow.

'Exit the villain, Black Baron Tyson!' Casually he settled a silky strand behind her ear, then he took her hand in a hard, masterful grip that left her little hope of breaking away, a toddler out for a stroll. 'You've got to learn, little one,' he said with his hard, mocking charm. 'But that's quite enough for one night. For me, at any rate. Let's rejoin the happy throng. One could wait an eternity for a simple thank-you.'

'Better still, I don't know what I could ever do without you!' she returned sweetly, and winced at the quick pressure on her hand.

It was a Christmas none of them were to forget, for with the dawn wind, Sir Joshua bowed out of life. No fuss, just a harsh little rattle, achieving in death what he had never done in life—a kind of peace for himself and his relatives. His grandson and his godson were ranged by his bed, drawn in the small hours, almost within minutes of one another, by that inexplicable instinct that warned them of a crisis for the Old Man.

'The final crisis and the end of an era!' Paul said bleakly, looking across the great canopied bed. He would never be able to come into this room again.

Gently Kyle drew the sheet over the Old Man's head. 'And farewell to my friend and a powerful influence. Sir Joshua Lynnton, a giant of a man!'

'He even died appropriately!' said Paul, swaying on his feet in a shocked daze, tears in his eyes had he known it. His hands were thrust deep into his luxurious dark blue robe. 'He had a charmed life in so many ways, though he was for ever on about his humble beginnings. Always a success, even at dying. Some suffer and suffer like my poor mother, and half his age. Was he your father, by any chance?'

Kyle almost flinched at the impact. 'God, how should I know? I wasn't there at the time. Do you have to go into it, Paul, right at this moment?'

'The presence of death sometimes forces things out of us. None of us have ever discussed it except to ourselves. I've carried on whole conversations with the bathroom mirror. We're a pretty extraordinary lot come to that. Don't take it so hard, old man. For years now I've thought of you as a brother, or a cousin or whatever the devil we are!'

'Oh, leave it alone, for God's sake. It all sounds pure farce. I don't believe the Old Man knew, in any case. The subject was never broached by me. It would have amounted to high treason. If any woman is to be believed, including my own mother whom I adored, then the answer is most definitely not. Does it matter? I'm here for better or worse.'

'No, I suppose not!' Paul pondered, then said quietly, 'You're a lot like him, all the same. Much more human, of course. I just thought you might know, and now is as good a time as any to say so. It could come out in the will. It will take years for the estate to be settled.'

'And a whole lot less for you to settle your affairs!' Kyle said tonelessly, his eyes on the sheeted figure. 'If we must start right over the Old Man's deathbed, it's about time you put your house in order. You can do it if you'd only get a drink out of your hand. It's been a nightmare watching you running downhill. Every dissatisfaction, every trifle and you drift off for a drink, and you know in your heart that's true. Not the big things, the small things have been getting you. Forget the fact I've missed out an enormous amount of support in the business.'

Paul's heavy, handsome face was momentarily obscured by his hand. 'I haven't got the brains, old son. Not the right kind of brains!'

'Oh, don't be a fool!' Kyle said softly. 'You've got judgment, flair, you know how to manipulate capital. You came up in a hard school!'

'I'm a small boy beside you! A bird in the hand does for me, but you see the whole bush!'

'Don't let that small detail inhibit your initiative. I

value your opinion, Paul, and I can do with your help. What's wrong with you anyway, man? This part you're playing is tedious and it's not even you!'

'That's right!' Paul said vaguely, still in a state of shock.

'But it's affecting us all!' Kyle punched the line home. 'Camilla, the children. Not Sir Joshua any more. Me. It's in your power to stop now, before the storm breaks. Don't tell me storms have a compulsive fascination for you?'

'Of course not!' Paul lifted his weary blue eyes. 'God, Kyle, don't you realise I'd give anything for even half of your zest! I can't think of another word. Oh, energy maybe, force of personality. You dominate. The Old Man did. I don't. Though once I too could tie the competition in knots!'

'And you can again, though you haven't done an honest day's work in years. Why, once you were one of the best athletes we ever had, and look at you now. Even with all the punishment you're inflicting on yourself you're still a handsome man. What *is* it you want? You've got a wife and a family, healthy, intelligent children. Position, money, a beautiful home. Maybe you've got too damned much. I've been alone ever since I can remember.'

'You? Alone?' Paul's tawny eyebrows almost shot to his hairline.

'Yes, on my own. Always. You have sisters, three of them, though you take precious little trouble to look them up.'

'That's Camilla's fault!' Paul mumbled. 'You know what she's like.'

'Oh, don't blame Camilla!' Kyle said with vivid scorn.

'You blame her for everything. You're a man, aren't you?'

'Oh yes, quite!' Paul almost sobbed, though it was meant to be a laugh. 'Man is synonymous with *master* to you, but I'm not like you, Kyle, half your luck!'

'Oh, stop it—you make me tired.'

'I could never take over the Organisation and that's flat!' Paul said pretty desperately as though a tremendous thought had just occurred to him.

'You won't have to, I can tell you that. But you can pull a hell of a lot more weight. I don't want all the load. I'm not the Old Man and I don't want to be. I don't equate happiness or what passes for it with money. I enjoy keeping the Organisation financially impregnable, but it's not the be-all and end-all of everything. That's not my real dream.'

But Paul wasn't listening, his mind was introverted. At last he looked up, meeting the silvery, lancing look. 'Do you really think I can do it? Camilla ...'

'... is your wife!' the younger man chopped him off neatly. 'The Old Man was only waiting for you to realise your potential. For God's sake can't you do it now when he's gone? You owe him everything, you know.'

'He was—he was really waiting?' There was a wealth of pathos in Paul's tone.

'Of course he was!' Kyle lied. 'He often spoke about it!'

'I thought he'd written me off.'

'What a fool you are, Paul. He loved you in his fashion.'

'Which wasn't as the rest of us. To the best of my knowledge the only person he ever cared for was your mother and maybe yourself. Forget the rest of us. My poor grandma, my old man because he was fool enough not to come home from the war, my sisters, my own kids. He didn't really care about any of us and that's a cold fact. He was a very hard man, my grandfather, but I shall miss him. Not a one of us measured up, except you. In a lot of ways I would have preferred just an ordinary old granddad.'

'Well, you sure didn't get one. There's no question about that!'

Across the bed Paul looked at the younger man. *All that splendid dark insolence!* Camilla called it. She didn't really know Kyle that well. It all of a sudden came to him. Kyle had a quality of heart the Old Man had quite missed out on. Maybe they'd never know who he was, but what did it mattter? He had truthfully said he thought of him as a brother. 'I'm not sure I know what to do next—Christmas, the children. Arrangements will have to be made.'

'I'll attend to all that!' Kyle said in his usual decisive fashion, and Paul smiled. He was like a prancing thoroughbred ready to up and win at the drop of a hat, extraordinarily spirited and vital.

'There'll be the devil to pay if Camilla doesn't get Sundown!' he said thoughtfully, his hand shifting to his face.

'Oh, hang Camilla!' Kyle said suddenly, lifting his head, his strange eyes alight. 'You're Paul Lynnton, Sir Joshua's grandson, Camilla as your wife will naturally benefit. But there's plenty of time for all that! Right at the moment I don't give a damn!'

'You were really fond of him, weren't you?' Paul said with some wonder. 'Much more so than I. I'm no hypocrite and he went out of his way to inflict plenty of smarting wounds.'

'Shake you up!' Kyle amended very smartly. 'If it was

tough for you, well, he was tough on himself. It was the only way he knew!'

'Yes!' Paul made a curious little sound. 'I'm sorry, old man. God, I'd better not say that. You're yourself. Shall I awaken Camilla?'

'I don't see why. It can wait until the morning. I'll start making calls now. I'll tell Gabriele in the morning. I don't think we need tell the children for a day or two. They can be got out of the house, for as long as it's necessary.'

Paul was standing, swaying slightly. 'Funny the fancy he took to Gabriele, right there at the end. Almost like an outsider winning the Cup!'

'Gabriele's no outsider!' Kyle said tersely. 'And she can charm the birds out of trees. Effortlessly, and I believe, sincerely.'

'An admission for you, old man!' Paul said with surprise, outspoken as ever.

'Perhaps,' Kyle said shortly. 'Now for the rest of the day, don't all of us keep getting in each other's way!'

'Leave it to me!' Paul said readily, 'and I won't think of a drink, don't worry. You can rely on me.'

There in his grandfather's room it had come to him that the need to make himself over was urgent and imperative. It was a job that could not wait. He could never dethrone Kyle and he did not want to. Such men earned their leadership—more, were born to it. He might not hold the Chair, but he would make an excellent right-hand man. His racing heart slowed and he wiped moisture from his palms. There was work to be done.

Gabriele awoke with the dawn wind, her mind very clear and alert, though what few hours' sleep she had had been troubled by weird, fragmentary dreams. She reached out a hand and turned the small porcelain bed-side clock towards her. Ten to five. Almost morning. She could sleep no longer. Sundown was calling her.

She got up and pulled her robe around her, a long yellow drift of silk. She wandered through the French doors to her outside balcony. The sky was the softest pearl grey, not yet flaming with gold and crimson on the horizon. Gabriele was shivering not so much with the faint dawn chill as the finger of premonition. Someone was moving down there in the courtyard, just walking in the cool, gem-frosted morning. She leant over the balcony and her heart almost stopped on her.

'Kyle!' she called out impulsively in the voice of sur-prise. He still wore his evening clothes, though the white ruffled shirt was carelessly buttoned. He hadn't been to bed at all. 'What in the world are you doing?'

'Walking. Come down!'

There was an odd note in the cool, dispassionate voice. Almost for a moment it had sounded like need. 'Just give me a moment!' She turned away and flung off her night-gown and robe, searching out slacks and a flower-sprigged halter-top. A brush through her hair and she was ready, stepping into her sandals.

He was waiting for her in the luminous morning, very dark and raffishly handsome and something else again. Sombre. He wasn't often that.

'What is it?' she asked quickly. 'Something's wrong, isn't it?'

'Sir Joshua!'

'Oh!' Gabriele stopped short as if he had struck her, then she went to him, fitting into the curve of his shoulder as his arm dropped around her.

'Let's walk.'

They walked for an hour and he never spoke. But he

wanted her there, Gabriele was certain of that, deeply grateful that they were together. The wind blew in their faces, carrying the earth's fragrance. The green curtain of trees enfolded them in the ordained stillness and silence. They might have been alone in a translucent world not yet awakened. Kyle was deeply preoccupied, but he still held her hand, fingers entwined.

In such a short time to be so deeply involved, to love a man to the exclusion of everything else. The real substance of her life. Yet it was hard to know who had changed her destiny. Kyle or Sir Joshua or both? Kyle had wanted her at Sundown. Sir Joshua had done the rest. Her aunt Camilla, her own flesh and blood, had not wanted her at all—worse, wished her gone. She could not think of tomorrow, only now with Kyle. The touch of his hand was a kind of completion.

All down the slopes like green waterfalls, the vines clustered to the ground, the sturdiest of plants, leafy and luxuriant—Sir Joshua's crown. Gabriele would always remember that. Soon the sun would be up, gilding and glossing the whole peaceful scene, ripening the grapes and developing the sugars. Another day!

The tall wrought iron gates of Sundown, delicate as butterfly wings, lay ahead of them. Together, on one impulse, they turned and retraced their steps back to the house. They had come far enough and the bleak part of the day was yet to come. Still, Gabriele's hand lay in Kyle's.

CHAPTER NINE

A FULL month later, Gabriele still had a crystal clear image of Camilla stalking out of the will-reading. She had not been named as a beneficiary, for as Sir Joshua clearly stated, she had received from him during his lifetime a small fortune in jewellery, paintings and antiques, and these she was to retain. As the wife of Paul Gilbert Lynnton, a major beneficiary, she would be more than amply provided for. Unfortunately Camilla viewed this as excessively stingy, a piece of calculated mischief quite in keeping with Sir Joshua's character and one she would never pardon. What might have been regarded as blessed good fortune by another, Camilla, with her colossal vanity, interpreted as an intolerable humiliation, and storm warnings flashed from her great eyes at this monstrous injustice. Her normally luscious red mouth was set in a thin, bright line. But the big, trembling upheaval was yet to come—Clause 4, dealing with the disposal of Sundown.

There had been a moment of complete incomprehension on the part of quite a few seated around the library, then Camilla's black eyes blazed outrage at Gabriele, who sat withdrawn in a far corner, an unwilling, humble participant in the whole business with the promise of Sundown for herself and her children and five thousand dollars a year for life. It was too much, a huge extravagance—certainly for Camilla, who considered herself publicly affronted. She was trembling with shock. Sundown, Sweet Sundown, her home, to pass into the hands of that little upstart! Her own impecunious niece—a bitter gibe. How he would have loved that, and her eyes flew to the deep-set dark eyes in the portrait, so lit with malicious pleasure, or so she thought. Each one in the library waited with varying reactions, expecting an hysterical outburst, Camilla to start screaming—anything. Clearly her wonderful control was tottering. But the poise of the years won out. In this her greatest defeat, Camilla emerged with dignity if not victorious, deserting them all, her stony, malevolent silence quite terrifying. Her husband, who didn't seem to care whether he bene-fited or not, quickly followed her as if she had hurled a summons at him, though she had never for an instant looked his way, tyrannously ruled, as he would be to the end.

Gabriele, her eyes huge and distressed, had sought Kyle's gaze for protection. He was seated in the big wing-backed chair under the portrait of Sir Joshua look-ing faintly irritated, for all an enormous bequest and the control of Sir Joshua's business holdings—extensive. Sir Joshua, on the other hand, appeared to be regarding them all with piercing good humour. George Cecil of the firm of Cecil, Warren and Cootes, the solicitors who handled the estate, looked over his spectacles until the disturbance subsided, then he continued as if nothing at all had happened, used to far worse outbursts, including faintings.

Ranged down the table from Paul's empty seat were his three sisters, handsome blondes, and their respective husbands, none of them in dire need, so there were no gasps of protest when several large grants were made to the University and well-known charitable organisations. Bequests to old friends and trusted servants so that in the end, only Camilla had been wounded and shocked be-yond recall as if it had only needed the clause about

Sundown to confirm that Sir Joshua, towards the end, had lost his sanity.

Gabriele had not even been given the opportunity to refuse her legacy, for Kyle had brushed her aside with a sardonic: 'Be still, child!' Sundown, in any case, he had assured her, was a tremendous responsiblity and one she would be unlikely to have to bother about until she was well into old age. 'Appease your conscience with that!' he had smiled at her so she hardly knew whether to take him seriously or not.

It hadn't taken him long to get down to the serious business, a piece of first-rate plotting with Joan Bradley née Lynnton, Paul's youngest sister, though charmingly he had left it to Joan to suggest to Gabriele that she should accompany the children to her husband's beautiful property in the sheep country of Victoria's Goulburn Valley. 'Aunt Joan,' as she wanted to be called, had children of her own, though they had never met their cousins, Melissa and Paul. This she wanted to remedy and at once, for she was a warm-hearted woman and very family-minded. It had grieved her that she had seen so little of the children and through no fault of her own. It had only required her brother's consent, which he gladly gave, Camilla being at that stage uncaring, and the deed was done. It was obvious to all that the children and Gabriele too would benefit from a temporary change of environment.

And so they did. The children revelled in this new way of life from the moment they drove through the gateway lined with poplars giving entrance to the beautiful property, a glory in spring when the wattles lit up the countryside for miles around, rivalling in their spectacular beauty the brilliant autumn hues of that same avenue of poplars. The trip was crammed with sightseeing. Tripping around the lush irrigated plains of the Goulburn Valley, the beautiful Ovens and King Valleys with their tobacco plantations and hop fields; Mount Buffalo, a great tourist attraction, soaring above one of the prettiest towns in Australia; Bright, an artist's paradise in the autumn with its colourful trees. They picnicked along the banks of the mighty Murray that flowed on fifteen hundred miles to the sea, they explored the fern gullies and the mountain streams and Uncle Ralph took them rainbow trout fishing in one of the famous streams, though he was the only one to catch anything.

On the property they learnt how to ride a horse, which probably meant that now their father would have to get them one. They got up very early for a dawn muster because sheep do not like to travel in the heat of the sun and they had to be well along the tracks before midday. They saw the prize merinos shorn and later tea, scones and pikelets with lashings of jam and cream in the cookhouse with the men. The children's cousins, Michael and Gavin, older certainly, were cheerful and tolerant, not averse to horseplay with their much younger cousins, and it was wonderful after all the antics to cool off in the lake that fronted the property.

Today they had all gone off to a neighbouring property ten miles down the road to present that family with the most lovable and most lustrous black labrador puppy Aunt Joan had ever bred—Augustus, and that was only his first name. Aunt Joan, among a dozen other things, was a very successful breeder and a knowledgeable judge at showtime and Augustus had a pedigree a mile long. As they were only out for an hour or so, Gabriele had elected to stay home. It was a lovely lazy day, heavy with summer, and she would take a dip without fear of being pushed in by one of the boys. From the moment of their meeting she had got on very well with her hostess, an easy-going countrywoman, warm-hearted and genuinely charming, devoted to her family and her beautiful home and property. The month on Amaroo Downs had proved very peaceful and harmonious, but soon it would be over. The children would be returning to Sundown, but what of Gabriele? That shattering interlude in her life was over.

She had a lot of thinking to do. All her hopes and desires, all the fantasies she had lived out these past few weeks she would have to erase from her mind. She was deeply, hopelessly in love, without even a glimpse of the man she loved and not likely to get one. It was pathetic but not unusual. Such things often happened, women being the way they were, only remotely related to men. Hectically busy, at the top of his profession, which after all was the main thing, Kyle had forgotten all about her. Yet only the mention of his name was enough to start her dreaming all over again. Aunt Joan mentioned him often because she was 'quite taken with him' and wanted him as a friend. As well she was endlessly grateful to him for providing her with the wonderful opportunity to get to know Paul's children, so physically like her, Paul especially, that every stranger they met on their trips took her for the children's mother. In her warming fashion, too, she had professed herself very grateful for Gabriele's company in a hitherto all-male household.

That day before she had left, puppy in hand, she had kissed Gabriele fondly on the cheek with the astonishingly comforting: 'Everything will come right in the end, you'll see!' Gabriele had coloured a little and stepped back to wave them off, smiling a little wryly at Melissa's: 'Be good!' She was rarely anything else and there was no opportunity for abandon. From now on she had better concentrate on essentials and leave alone the thought of Kyle Tyson. She had examinations to pass in order to equip herself for life. Sir Joshua's great generosity had for ever removed from her the burden of insecurity, but she had her own way to make. She had the temperament and soon she would have the necessary qualifications for a teaching career—High School, English or History. Why didn't she feel happier? It would have been greatly too much to expect a man like Kyle Tyson to share her wild but never adolescent yearnings. And now she had done it again—thought of him. So time-consuming! Continents had never been discovered that way. Men were the originals and they took a much better view of romantic alliances. They simply 'went through'. And thinking this she turned away.

Down at the lake it was blissfully and deliciously cool—the sun through the trees, a flash-lit brilliance. Swiftly Gabriele twined her hair into a plait and secured it on top of her head, then she dived in, cleaving the clear, bracingly cool water. Grass daisies, white and yellow, grew thickly to the water's edge, lined by big shady paperbarks, Murray pines and scores of feathery wattles. Along the glossy branches of the tallest trees, birds were gliding in and out, chattering, making love, the brilliant flash of their plumage like jewel colours amid the green.

Later, as she lay on her thick sapphire beach towel, a soft sensuous sigh rippled up from her throat. She was lying, a slender golden arrow, in a broad segment of sunwash that was quickly drying her silver-gilt pigtail. Long hours of sunlight had turned her limbs to a smooth even gold she was rather proud of. The air was heavy with the sweet, musky scent of the bush and she filled her lungs with it. It was a miracle, nature, the deepest, ever constant source of comfort and simple, uncomplicated pleasure. One was rich indeed with the trees, the tall swishing grasses, the deep lucent green of the lake, the peacock blue dome that arched above them, the bell-toned bird song. All heavenly! Gabriele relaxed against the towel, undersprung with thick grass. Her tranquillity was deceptive, but she was already half way asleep.

There was no escape even in dreams, a particularly tenacious dream. She couldn't shake it at all. But it *wasn't* a dream!

'Kyle!' She shot up, staring at him for all the dislocating shock.

'Yes, Kyle!' he said idly. 'Fancy seeing you here, Gabriele. On this hot summer day. The idea!'

Tall, very lean, the same way she had remembered him. Casual perfection. A thinly striped cotton shirt, beige slacks, a seersucker jacket in a matching plaid, all yellows and blacks and tans. She would have loved to have told him he looked great, but she didn't.

'How long have you been there?' she asked, the sheer shimmering colour washing up under her skin.

'The whole summer, I think.' She was moving backwards instinctively in some confusion, looking for her yellow jersey kimono jacket. Some protection! Lazily he helped her out with his longer reach. 'Here, this is what you're looking for, I think, though I much prefer you as you are!' She was still confused, her mind and her body not working at all well together, but he didn't appear to notice. 'Camilla wants her children home again. She's quite ready for them,' he informed her lazily.

'Why didn't Paul come?' she parried. Kyle's presence there was an incalculable mystery—or miracle, but she allowed herself no hopes of anything.

'Paul,' he drawled, 'is at the moment entirely devoted to rejuvenating his hitherto impossible marriage. I wish him well. I'm sure you do too. Won't I do as well, for all you're looking at me as if I'm the last flaming straw!'

Her eyes in their dark density of lashes were startlingly clear. 'How could you think that?' she protested. 'I'm still in arrears with events, that's all. Put it down to the sun on my head. I never expected to see you at all. We've had the most marvellous time. The children have loved it. They're well and happy. And Joan and Ralph have been so very kind.'

'Yes, I've heard all about it from Joan,' he said, his eyes lingering on her face.

'Are they back, then?' she inquired, wondering just how long she had been asleep.

'Not as yet,' he supplied. 'One of the hands saw me arrive and directed me down here. One wonders why! I was speaking to Joan last night on the telephone, if that answers the wide-eyed look,' he added, his tone half sardonic, half amused.

'Oh! She didn't mention it!' Gabriele looked down, creamy nape like a sacrificial lamb. She was feeling, not mistakenly, that he was annoyed with her, some irrelevant rush of anger men were prone to.

His tone was deliberate, very resonant. 'Possibly because I asked her not to. For all I knew you might have taken it into your head to flit off, like that little crimson chat up there!'

There was a definite edge in his voice and she hurried into speech, semi-apologetic, though she couldn't for the life of her see what she was apologising about. 'But why should I do that?'

'You answer that!' he said crisply, coolly polite. 'The

same way you failed to drop me one line in a whole month, I suppose. A postcard would have done—one of these idyllic pastoral scenes, you among the sheep. Forget the love and kisses bit.'

'But I never thought for a moment you'd be expecting any!' she said artlessly, her eyes on the ground. His long legs were firmly planted beside her. Nice shoes, she thought, examining them with a troubled air. 'I just didn't think of it at all.'

'What have you been thinking of, then, if one might enquire?'

'Passing my exams!' she supplied effortlessly what was not true. 'I hope to take up teaching eventually, you know!'

'Really? How wonderfully rewarding!' He picked up a pebble and threw it quite viciously into the lake.

'It's my decision, Kyle.'

'Is it?' He turned to regard her, one black brow winging. 'I thought someone else ruled your life.'

'I don't understand you!' She looked at him quickly and then wished she hadn't, for the sight of him made her heart turn over and it wasn't right yet. She had no such effect on him, for he picked up another stone, feeling the weight of it in his palm before taking aim.

'It seems very much like it, doesn't it? You have a beautiful tan, I suppose that's something. Some justification for all the long days, and I'm sure you went to bed early. The sun has bleached your hair to silver, did you know? You're a charming child altogether, but no manners. I can't understand that in your mother's child. She was one of the most charming women I've ever met. Tell me, what are you going to do about Sundown?'

'What can I do?' she asked, her heart beating very fast. 'That was Sir Joshua's idea. The sword of Damocles over Camilla's head, I think. I'll sign it over to her if you like!'

Kyle gave a muffled little sound very difficult to interpret and she went on, rather tragically. 'Can you arrange it for me? Your solicitor—Mr. Cecil, isn't it?'

'What a damn fool thing!' he said disagreeably.

'It's not really mine!' Gabriele said fretfully. She was oddly keyed up, ready to dive right back into the lake and never come up, at least until he was gone. Then she would come out and break her heart on the bank. 'Aunt Camilla loves it,' she cried. 'I don't care. Oh, I *do*, but I could never keep it up anyway.'

'Oh, stop,' he said briskly. 'You're wringing my heartstrings. What a strange child you are! The old man knew what he was doing, none better. It was his house, after all, and those few telling conditions will keep Camilla in line. As you so rightly said, she loves it. The house is the ideal background for all her objets d'art. Where else would she put them, do you know? In a museum? There aren't too many houses around like Sundown. It would cost a fortune to build today and you want to give it away. What a strange child!' he said again.

To be treated in turns as a child and an adult. He should be ashamed of himself! She clenched her small even teeth. 'If you call me a child just one more time, I shall hit you hard! That's a promise, and you wouldn't like that. I've told you for the last time, I'm a woman!'

'You're not!' he said forcibly, and pulled her into his arms. He laughed suddenly, his eyes gleaming at her outraged expression. 'Not a thinking woman, at any rate! More like a dryad. Silk for hair, flower petals for skin. You smell wildly fresh like growing things. The green lake!' He buried his face in the soft velvety skin at the base of her throat, and she trembled visibly and tried to push away.

'You're perfect for this kind of thing!' she said, softly severe as though she was glimpsing Dante's Inferno.

'Oh? What's that?' He lifted his head, his silver eyes very lazy and misleading.

'*Dalliance!*' she pronounced with defenceless young scorn.

'Come now, Gabriele, I've no doubt you've had tons of experience yourself!'

She hit out at him and he caught her hand. 'Gabriele, you're enchanting and mysteriously stupid. I can't see how you'll ever take up that career of yours. You've too much to learn yourself!'

'And you're going to teach me?'

'Did I say so?' His eyes moved over her, very masculine and assessing. 'You're much, much too young for my possessing, though I rarely shirk a challenge.'

'I wonder you're in any at all! It would be unthinkable, unspeakable, for you to get caught in one of your own traps, and I'm wishing it on you. For someone else to be the centre of your existence, but who else is there, now Camilla is settling for Sundown?'

Too late she remembered herself. Kyle drew an audible breath and his white teeth snapped. 'Normally I don't care what anyone says about me, but you made a bad error in judgment there, my lake-eyed little puritan!'

'I'm sorry. Forgive me!' she said with the first pang of shame and the bone-cracking pain of his hands on her shoulders.

'You've got a lot of chance of that!' he said softly. 'Either you don't write at all or you talk yourself out of existence!'

Her eyes seemed to dilate and she swallowed nervously. 'I said I'm sorry and I am. I can't help it.

There's no progress for me at all when you're around. I hardly know what I'm saying, fretting to death wanting you!'

His hands fell away from her with ludicrous abruptness. 'You can't mean that?'

'All right, I don't mean it at all!' she said wildly, her mouth trembling, her long legs digging into the thick turf trying to get up.

'You're not going anywhere,' he said, softer still, calmly conversational. 'This is just getting interesting!'

'For you, maybe. I detest wasting time. I'm off!' She was seized by a great agitation. It didn't seem possible, but she had broken his hold, clear of him, fleeing up the bank, slender golden legs flashing, long hair whipped into silky skeins, blinding her.

It wasn't a bad effort, all things considered, but as she neared the top and comparative safety, an arm came around her narrow waist, like honed steel. It locked, cruelly implacable, a prison without doors, or keys or anything. He was fully aroused, man, the eternal hunter, spinning her round in his arms, twining his hand through the loosened coils of her plait, jerking her head back into the curve of his shoulder. Gabriele opened her mouth to cry out in an involuntary frenzy, but he was kissing her over and over, bent on feeding his own mounting hunger, a selfish consuming fire, and a furious contempt for his own desire.

Her tormented limbs were trembling, refusing to support her, her mind spinning in a permanent giddy yearning. With a violent little exclamation Kyle suddenly swept her up and carried her back down the bank towards the lake's edge. Gabriele fully expected anything —murder; she had a terrifying vision of herself strangled with her own hair; once before he had threatened her. Or

186

thrown bodily into the lake, drowned, Ophelia floating downstream with flowers twined in her hair, a ghostly swan. His dark face above her supported all this melodrama, rather terrifyingly hard and handsome, unyielding like a classic carving, the light eyes coldly brilliant flashing equal parts of scorn and desire all over her and a smattering of downright hate! Perhaps he did hate her. Obviously she had aroused some fairly powerful instincts. She had insulted him, of course, and he was the complete autocrat by nature and circumstance. There was no worse dictator.

Her horror increased violently as he came to a halt, almost pushing her to the ground, then lowered himself beside her, powerful, lean and vital. 'I can't believe you want to hurt me,' she said in an inadequate nervous frenzy, for he had gone far beyond any thought of gallantry. His strength was frightening and exciting too and she was receiving these sensations in alternating dizzy waves.

'I'm in no fit state to be courteous, if that's what you mean!' Kyle said curtly. 'The simple truth is my need of you has gone far beyond what you're capable of giving, and unlike you, Gabriele, I know what I'm talking about. A whole month and not even a line! To my sorrow it's been brought home to me that I simply have to have you around. In fact I'll go a bit further and say I just don't want to live without you and I don't intend to.'

'But I had no idea!' she said faintly.

'Why, are you so damned childish?'

'Oh, how unfair! You never wrote to me. You spoke to Joan and you never spoke to me ...'

'My dear girl,' he chopped her off emphatically, 'unlike you, who have been basking in the sun and gilding that velvety soft skin, I've been working a twenty-four-hour day. I've only just made up my mind to stop and I've only just made up my mind I simply can't wait until such time as you mature. I just could be mad by then!'

'Wait for what?' She twisted around to look up at him, the stiff-necked, proud as Lucifer ...

'... marriage, you silly goose,' he said grimly, and pulled her into his arms again.

'And you think I'll fall into your arms on command?'

'You seem to have done,' he pointed out suavely. 'A pushover!'

Tears welled into her eyes and he groaned and gathered her to him, kissing her mouth and her throat and her eyes. 'I'm sorry. I'm sorry, Gabriele. I don't mean that at all! Does it make it any better if I tell you I love you? I've never said that to a woman before, for all my various affairs which I'm quite sure you've heard about. Camilla wasn't one of them. Incredibly sexy as she is, I still found the strength to resist her. It wasn't all that difficult. Intuitively you should have known that. Such an impossible situation! I thought I was an old hand at self-preservation, but even that seems to have gone by the board.'

'So you resent me?' she said with a faintly sad smile. 'Loving me, I mean, if you do love me at all. I can't seem to grasp it.'

'You will!' he said dryly. 'We're only sitting on a river bank with the family due home at any time. Inhibiting —just as well!' He touched a gentle finger to her softly parted mouth. 'And just to prove how much I love you, you may continue your studies after we're married. I've no real objection to an intellectual wife, though I see no obvious signs of it. Say you love me,' he said urgently, low-voiced. 'Go on, say it at once. I have to warn you now that I have a difficult nature!'

'I can see that quite well!' She smiled at him with unquestioned surrender. 'Perhaps you'll have mellowed by the time our son arrives!'

Brilliant lights invaded his eyes. 'Don't you believe it!' he said with hard mockery, and bent her back into his arms. 'You're mine ... mine ... mine, and I'll never change. I've been plotting to get you ever since I laid eyes on you, Gabriele my angel. As much of a woman as I'll ever want. There, I've said it and I meant it!'

Breathlessly she said: 'Kyle!' every secret of her heart in her face. She heard the quick intake of his breath, then her eyelashes fell, once more to surrender to this matchless golden tide. It wasn't necessary to tell him she loved him at all. He knew, directly and with passion, that what was between them was real and would last with a faithfulness and consistency few would achieve.

She was happy, happy, on a peak of intensity for which there were no adequate words and none needed for lovers for whom the whole world is transformed. Kyle had taken the whole course of her life out of her hands. She was committed and it was a rapture, a surrender, and the greatest gift of all. Life was a precious gift and man and woman incomparable creations, incomplete the one without the other. What had been said before so perfectly would be said many times again:

'Though much is taken, much abides!'

Gabriele's life had come right again. That summer at Sundown.

Why the smile?

... because she has just received her **Free Harlequin Romance Catalogue!**

... and now she has a complete listing of the many, many Harlequin Romances still available.

... and now she can pick out titles by her favorite authors or fill in missing numbers for her library.

You too may have a **Free Harlequin Romance Catalogue** (and a smile!), simply by mailing in the coupon below.

Catalogue of available titles is revised every three mont[h]

Have You Missed Any of These
Harlequin Romances?

xx

Have You Missed Any of These
Harlequin Romances?

Y